AGRICULTURE IN WALES
DURING THE NAPOLEONIC WARS

Parish of *Coyty* —————————— in the Diocese of *Landaff*

	Number of Acres.	GENERAL REMARKS.
Wheat	264.	In my humble opinion, too great a monopoly of farms is injurious to the public welfare, oppressive to the
Barley	190.	poor, and destructive of the public markets and fair
Oats	89.	dealing, and tends greatly to enhance the price of all sorts of provisions, &c. And I am further of opinion,
Potatoes	14.	that the cultivation of waste land, under proper regulation
Peas	6	may be of great advantage, as a means of increasing the wealth of the Nation, by exciting a spirit of industry
Beans	.....	amongst the lower class of people, by preventing emigration, and by promoting a love of one's Country, with many
Turnips or Rape	5.	other social and relative virtues, which are essentially necessary to constitute the happiness of mankind.—

Tho. Davies, Rector of Coyty

Printed by A. Strahan, Printers-Street, London.

Glamorganshire.

The Acreage Return of 1801 for the parish of Coety, Glamorgan
(SOURCE: P.R.O., H.O.67, 13)

AGRICULTURE IN WALES DURING THE NAPOLEONIC WARS

A study in the geographical interpretation of historical sources

BY

DAVID THOMAS

CARDIFF
UNIVERSITY OF WALES PRESS
1963

PRINTED IN GREAT BRITAIN
BY WILLIAM LEWIS (PRINTERS) LTD., CARDIFF

I'M PLANT
SIÂN A HUW

Cân yr hwsmon trafferthus

Trwy'ch cenad bob hwsmon naws dirion dysdewch,
Fy hanes a'm herlid a'm gofyd a gewch;
'Rwy braidd wedi blino yn ceibio pob cae,
Pan ddyallodd y nghalon y moddion y mae.
Rhaid teilo hyd y tîr, dal yr arad yn hir,
Prynu cyrch hadyd, trwy g'ledfyd yn glir,
Llyfnu prydnhawn; gwneud pob peth yn iawn,
Codi cloddiau newydd, yn rhesi hyd y rhosydd,
Y myned tua'r haf-ddydd i fynydd am fawn,
Ac yno trin gwair, a phob ffwndwr ffair,
A gweision i'm canlyn, at drin bara ac enllyn,
Rhaid cadw dwy forwyn, tra dygyn neu dair.

Medi ar ol hyny a'i ddyrnu fo o'i ddas,
Ac anwyd o berfedd a gwinedd y gwas,
A'r hogyn yn rhegi, dan boeni am gael bwyd,
A'r forwyn un amser o'i chader ni chwyd.
A'r wraig gyda'i thê, yn llawen ei lle,
Ni fu y fath aflwydd trwy'r gwledydd ag ê,
A minau yn fy *nghlocks* yn erlid y *roques*.
Rhai ddyfro rhai i garthu a rhai yn mron rhynu,
Mae llawer yn haeddu mewn beudy gael *box*
'Rol gwerth'r dâ'i gyd, meddwl byw'n glyd,
Ni's gwn os ydwy yma o gantoedd pwy gynta,
Sy'n disgwl oddi wrtha, eu bara'n yn y byd.

ANONYMOUS BALLAD,
(Trefriw, late eighteenth century).

The song of the troubled farmer

Pray silence good brothers who slave at the soil,
I'll tell you the worries that harry my toil:
Bone-tired I struggle to till every field,
But my heart breaks to see how little they yield.
Manuring now and long holding the plough
And buying new oats with the sweat of my brow.
Harrowing at noonday, making ship-shape and neat,
    Building fences galore in rows on the moor;
Then away every summer to the mountain for peat.
And soon comes the hay, all work and no play,
    With no man at his ease: and for loaves and a cheese
One needs three stout women to toil night and day.

And then the corn harvest and threshing the rick,
With frost biting belly and nails to the quick;
The lad cursing loud for his bit of a crust
While the servant girl holds to her chair in the dust.
The wife at her tea, well contented is she:
Was there ever a worried mortal like me?
I rave and I stamp to hurry each scamp
    To the water hard by, to the stable and sty;
A bed in the cowshed each deserves like a tramp.
After tilling my land I can't understand
    Why hundreds around can always be found,
And each man expecting his bread from my hand.

WIL IFAN

PREFACE

DURING the eighteenth century the chief means of distributing news and opinions in rural Wales was the ballad. Apart from a few short-lived magazines and some denominational periodicals there were no vernacular newspapers—*Seren Gomer*, the pioneer paper of Joseph Harris, did not first appear until 1814—and so published ballads form one of the major sources of information upon life and conditions in agricultural areas before the beginning of the Napoleonic wars in 1793. In a ballad such as *Cân yr hwsmon trafferthus* (*The song of the troubled farmer*), printed in Trefriw, Caernarvonshire, at the end of the eighteenth century by Ishmael Davies, the anonymous author has given in the colloquial idiom of the day an adequate description of the farmer's lot. In the first two stanzas, quoted above, the difficulties of rural life are made clear and a certain amount of information emerges: crops and agricultural methods are mentioned and the enclosure of wasteland is suggested. But the ballads are distorted mirrors of agricultural conditions; at best they provide an incomplete commentary, at worst they proclaim biased opinions.

It is fortunate that for the period of the Napoleonic wars a great deal of additional material is available as a result of surveys of various kinds; there can have been few other times in British history when such frantic and diverse efforts were made to catalogue the state of agriculture. This information provides the greatest possible contrast with that for the years before the wars, not only in volume but also in its detail, objectivity, and coverage. In a consideration of the period the allusions of the ballads, together with the material to be found in a number of other limited sources, can be ignored in favour of the more tangible evidence of the surveys. It is with the surveys that this work deals. The period 1793–1815 is also of special concern because it was a time of exceptional economic, political, and social conditions. The intrinsic interest of the years provides a further reason why the abundant material available should be used to make a period reconstruction. Unfortunately the picture which emerges is fragmentary. The surveys do not always give information uniform in quality or quantity about all aspects of agriculture, for example, the great volume of material on tillage is out of all proportion to the area occupied by crops in Wales at this time, and the difficulties involved in the use of the surveys are various. It has seemed better in each chapter to deal with one major source rather than to attempt a chronological narrative, to follow a strictly regional approach, or to study systematically each facet of agriculture. In this way particular attention can be paid to the problems of interpretation and to the methods by which these are best resolved.

The orthography of Welsh place-names always presents difficulties and this is specially true at present when the Ordnance Survey is revising the spelling shown on its maps. In this text the spellings are those given in *A gazetteer of Welsh place-names* (Cardiff, 1958), edited by Dr. Elwyn Davies. Where acceptable Anglicized or English names exist, these have been used; otherwise the correct Welsh spelling will be found. The spelling of many place-names is different from that in current Ordnance Survey sheets, where debased forms still abound, but in no instance does this hinder the identification of places.

Throughout the work *Wales* should be understood to include Monmouthshire.

ACKNOWLEDGMENTS

Many people have given generous help during the preparation of this study. Professor David Williams of the Department of Welsh History, University College of Wales, Aberystwyth, and Mr. J. Gareth Thomas, Registrar of the University of Wales, have read the manuscript and made many useful suggestions, for which I am greatly indebted to them. At University College London, most of my colleagues in the Department of Geography have, at various times, offered advice which I have been glad to accept, but I should particularly like to record my thanks to Professor H. C. Darby and Dr. J. T. Coppock, both of whom read and commented upon the full text. Others have readily replied to queries I have made: Mr. Harold Carter, Aberystwyth, Dr. Margaret Davies, Cardiff, Professor A. H. Dodd, Bangor, Mr. G. E. Fussell, Sudbury, Dr. S. Gregory, Liverpool, Mrs. Daphne Harris, London, Mr. T. I. Jeffreys–Jones, Harlech, Dr. L. S. Pressnell, London, and Professor William Rees, Cardiff. To the Rev. William Evans I owe gratitude for the English version of the ballad with which this work begins and to Mr. Kenneth J. Wass, for the care he has taken in drawing the maps and diagrams. I would like to thank my wife who undertook all the typing required in preparing the text, helped check proofs, and assisted in compiling the index. Finally, my thanks go to the officers of the University Press for their skill and thoughtfulness.

The research upon which the work is based was assisted by a grant from the Maconochie Foundation, which is here gratefully acknowledged.

DAVID THOMAS

University College London,
Calan Gaef, 1962

CONTENTS

LIST OF ILLUSTRATIONS

ACKNOWLEDGMENT is gratefully made to the following for permission to reproduce illustrations:

The Controller of Her Majesty's Stationery Office (frontispiece, Figs. 13, 17).
The Director-General, Ordnance Survey (Figs. 13, 17).
The Secretary, Royal Meteorological Society (Fig. 14a).
Dr. S. Gregory (Fig. 14b).
The Director, Geological Survey and Museum (Fig. 17).
Professor William Rees and Faber and Faber Ltd. (Fig. 40).

I. THE SETTING

CHAPTER 1

ECONOMIC, POLITICAL, AND SOCIAL BACKGROUND

THE turn of the eighteenth century was a time of great change. While the growth of industry was creating and modifying the urban landscape, in the countryside equally striking transformations resulted from a set of economic, political, and social forces. In Wales agricultural improvement had in some respects lagged behind that in other parts of Britain, and consequently the effects of these forces were particularly marked. The painfully slow progress of the preceding centuries gave way to changes at a bewildering rate.

From an economic point of view the period of the Napoleonic wars was exceptional. In his Preface to the *Census* of 1831, John Rickman tabulated the average price of wheat per customary Winchester quarter at Windsor market for each year from 1595 to 1833.[1] The values between 1730 and 1830 have been plotted in Fig. 1 and a trend line inserted to smooth out short-term fluctuations. From the graph it is clear that the price of wheat in 1801 (£7 4s. 7d.) was the highest over the whole period, and the price in 1800 very little lower. On only three previous occasions had the price exceeded £4; in 1795, 1796, and 1799. The trend line illustrates well the way in which the general rise in wheat prices coincided with the wartime period. Other sources suggest that these figures are typical of movements in the price of wheat over the country as a whole,[2] and also that the prices of other crops, such as barley, oats, rye, peas, and beans were affected in the same way, though increases in price were not quite as pronounced.[3] The year 1801 thus marks the peak of a period of acute inflation in the prices of arable products.

The price of grain was to some extent controlled by institutional mechanisms. The complicated body of legislation which grew up as the Corn Laws was intended to encourage the growth of grain in

---

[1] *Census 1831*, li–lii.

[2] W. F. Galpin, *The grain supply of England during the Napoleonic period* (New York, 1925), 213–19.

[3] Cf. J. E. Thorold Rogers, *A history of agriculture and prices in England* (Oxford, 1902), VII, 225–9; with, 'An account of the grain of all sorts . . . in each year from January 5th, 1800, to January 5th, 1825', *Parliamentary Papers*, 20 (1825), 234–61.

Britain so that the country could be self-sufficient and capable of an export surplus. This was achieved by two methods. A sliding scale of duties, geared to the market price at home, was imposed on

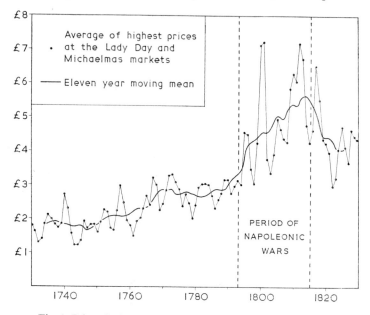

Fig. 1. Price of wheat per quarter at Windsor market, 1730–1830
(Source: *Census 1831*)

imported grain; when the home price was low, the duty was heavy, and when the price was high, the duty was nominal. A corn bounty was also paid on exported grain when prices in Britain were low. This, in effect, prevented the glutting of the home market with surplus grain. Although the price levels at which controls operated changed from time to time, the principle remained the same from the middle of the seventeenth century until 1814.[1] In times of shortage the inevitable upward movement of prices should have been checked when import duties eased and the export bounty ceased to be paid, thus encouraging imports and discouraging exports. That this did not happen at the turn of the century signifies the strength of the inflation.

[1] D. G. Barnes, *A history of the English Corn Laws from 1660 to 1846* (London 1930), *passim*.

The causes of the inflation were manifold, as the pamphleteers of the time were eager to point out.[1] Clearly the immediate cause was the succession of poor harvests in the last decade of the century[2] which led to severe grain shortages at home. Such was the dearth of corn that in each year from 1793 to 1801 the Corn Laws were suspended. The particularly bad harvests of 1794 and 1795 led to the reversal of the bounty system and instead of bounties being paid for export, they were paid for wheat imports. In addition, the export of wheat was forbidden and the manufacture of starch and hair powder from grain prohibited. The situation was aggravated by the coincidence of famine years in this country with those on the Continent, where inflation was also being experienced.[3] In the circumstances, relief from the Napoleonic empire could hardly be expected.

The outbreak of war with France in 1793 could in itself be considered a factor leading to increases in prices. It was estimated in 1804 by Lord Hawkesbury that over 10 per cent of the population of military age in the British Isles was in the army or navy.[4] Not only had these men to be equipped, clothed, and fed, but the productive workers of the country who supplied their needs were reduced in numbers. Goods of all sorts were much in demand and in short supply, and consequently inflationary pressure was created. The war involved the government in great additional expenditure which had to be met by taxation, and as much as one-sixth of the national income may have been absorbed in this way. In 1799 Pitt was forced to introduce income tax, but direct taxation never formed the major source of government revenue, even though this form of taxation was less likely to lead to a rise in prices. The greatest source of revenue was indirect taxation,[5] mainly in the form of customs and excise duties, which automatically increased the prices of commodities. A third way in which the war affected grain prices was in the restriction of overseas supply. Undoubtedly the war interfered with grain production on the Continent and it was

[1] Ibid., 78.
[2] B. H. Higgins, 'Agriculture and the war; a comparison of agricultural conditions in the Napoleonic and World War', *Agricultural History*, 14 (1940), 9.
[3] A Young, 'An enquiry into the rise of prices in Europe', *Annals of Agriculture*, 46 (1815), 139–219.
[4] J. Lowe, *The present state of England in regard to agriculture, trade and finance* (London, 1822), 45.
[5] A. Hope-Jones, *Income tax in the Napoleonic wars* (Cambridge, 1939), 112.

also part of Napoleon's policy to prevent grain reaching Britain, though this policy was not pursued consistently and licensed trading in surplus grain was allowed at certain times during the war. But more important, as Galpin has stressed, was the psychological effect of the restrictions in supply.[1] In comparison with the grain used in this country, the quantity imported was relatively small and cutting off some of the overseas supply should not, in itself, have caused such a severe inflation. But when viewed against the background of the known shortages at home, news of restricted overseas trade in grain assumed great importance in the minds of Britons, many of whom believed starvation to be inevitable. It is easy to understand how in a mood of near-hysteria the prices of agricultural provisions rose.

With a rapidly growing industrial population in the eighteenth century Britain had become a net importer of grain, and consequently more and more susceptible to economic influences from outside. The loss of agricultural self-sufficiency, combined with war shortages, led to a balance of payments crisis during which large quantities of gold passed from London to other countries in order to settle outstanding accounts. While gold reserves were low, a small French landing near Fishguard in 1797 caused a run on the banks which they were unable to meet. The Bank of England therefore suspended the redemption of its notes in gold. An inconvertible paper currency in its turn led to a great increase in the number of notes in circulation, allowed a rise in the price of gold bullion, and aggravated the inflation. Today, this increase in bank paper is generally deemed to have been necessary and inevitable, but at the time it produced widespread criticism of the government's fiscal policy, which found expression both in the official report of the House of Commons 'Bullion Committee' in 1810 and in the writings of such men as David Ricardo.[2] Arthur Young was among those who supported the government's rejection of the 'Bullion Report'.[3] It was not until well after the war, in 1821, that the gold standard was reintroduced.

---

[1] W. F. Galpin, op. cit., 13–14.

[2] M. J. Silberling, 'Financial and monetary policy of Great Britain during the Napoleonic wars: II, Ricardo and the Bullion Report', *Quarterly Journal of Economics*, 38 (1923–24), 397–439.

[3] A. Young, 'An enquiry into the progressive value of money in England', *Annals of Agriculture*, 46 (1812), 65–137.

Court has argued that the sharp rise in prices was due to the economic policies pursued by the government during the war.[1] While it was concerned with the wartime scarcity and with the distressed state of the poor, it felt little moral obligation to interfere more than was politically expedient with a free economy. To do otherwise would have contradicted the teachings of the new political economy so recently pioneered in the works of Hume and Adam Smith. High prices themselves, it was contended, solved the conflicting claims upon the economy by excluding the weakest customers from the market. Commodities which had once satisfied civilian needs were thus freed for war uses. Whether today this is considered sound economic argument, or whether the government's attitude is attributed to the fact that the landlords who sat at Westminster had everything to gain from rising prices not matched by rises in agricultural wages, is irrelevant. Whatever the rationale of government thinking, the fact is that curbing the inflation was never the object of national finance and so, in a negative if not in a positive way, government policy contributed towards the sharp rise in prices.

The results of the wartime inflation were as varied as its causes. Agriculture was greatly stimulated by the high prices being offered for foodstuffs and especially by the high prices of grain. There can be little doubt that the maximum amount of suitable land, and a great deal that would normally have been considered unsuitable, was put under the plough.[2] But not all the increased output came from extensions of the arable area; some of the increase was the result, as in more recent wars, of the greater efficiency with which the existing arable land was worked. Naomi Riches has described how the agricultural revolution in East Anglia was well under way by the middle of the eighteenth century.[3] It was not until the end of the century that these improvements became widely adopted in other parts of the country, under the stimulus of inflated prices and as a result of the energies of such men as Young, Sinclair, and Marshall. The more advanced farm machinery, the improved rotations, especially the popular Norfolk four-course, the scientific

---

[1] W. H. B. Court, *A concise economic history of Britain from 1750 to recent times* (Cambridge, 1954), 144–50.

[2] R. E. Prothero (Lord Ernle), *English farming past and present* (London, 1936), 318.

[3] N. Riches, *The agricultural revolution in Norfolk* (Chapel Hill, 1937).

breeding, the better systems of drainage, and the new fertilizers all helped to increase output, but they also lowered production costs. Every incentive thus existed for farmers to adopt the improved methods, though it is possible that the ease with which profits could be made had the opposite effect upon some, however much this was contrary to the spirit of the time. Many of the new techniques modified the countryside greatly and this is reflected in contemporary statistics, maps, and writings. When examining this evidence for Wales it will be of interest to trace to what extent the fresh agricultural ideas had modified a landscape which was not only distant, but very different, both physically and culturally, from that in which they had developed in eastern England.

The need for more home-grown food during the war was also met by speeding up the enclosure of open fields and waste; a process which had been under way for many centuries and one which was particularly sensitive to changes in the price of grain.[1] The movement was given official encouragement in the belief that the whole rural population would benefit, but, in fact, many suffered. There were great differences between the enclosure of open fields and the enclosure of waste, but the social effects were often the same. Though enclosure was not generally a primary cause of depopulation, in many areas it accelerated the drift away from the land of the small-scale farmers who could not afford the often considerable costs of enclosure, or who could not compete with those occupying larger farms. It also diminished the prospects of the small farmers who remained. What opportunities there had been for additional income were removed with the apportionment of the common land.[2] Consequently the large estates grew while the smallholders tended to become labourers, either in industry or agriculture. At the very time when increasing numbers of agricultural workers were becoming dependent upon their wages alone, essential foods were increasing rapidly in price.[3] Although wages eventually rose in sympathy the difficulties of rural labour were such that in 1795 the Berkshire justices at Speenhamland evolved a sliding scale of poor relief to supplement wages, based upon the price of bread and the

[1] See diagram, G. T. Griffith, *Population problems of the age of Malthus* (Cambridge, 1926), 179.
[2] W. Cunningham, *The growth of English industry and commerce in modern times* (Cambridge, 1921), II, 713–15.
[3] See diagram, J. H. Clapham, *An economic history of modern Britain* (Cambridge, 1950), I, 128.

size of the family. Very quickly the Speenhamland system became widely used throughout southern Britain in an attempt to relieve the distress of agricultural workers.

Fig. 2. Shires and streams

Many contemporary writers, led by Malthus, attributed not only the rise in prices but also the great increase in population, probably the most outstanding social phenomenon of the late eighteenth century, to the relief of the poor which, by increasing wages, was said to allow larger families. This idea is not now accepted,[1] and it

[1] See discussion, W. H. B. Court, op. cit., 8–13.

is far more likely that the drift away from the land, which continued
after the Speenhamland system began, had ultimately far more
influence upon the growth, and certainly upon the redistribution, of
population, though this was only one of many components in the
change. No great accuracy can be expected in population statistics
before 1801, when the first enumeration took place, but a number
of estimates allow the trends which existed to be recognised. The
most detailed and trustworthy figures are those of Rickman, who
produced two series of estimates[1] derived from a study of parish
records of baptisms, burials, and marriages.[2] In the second series he
published the county totals for England only. From the earlier,
though not necessarily less reliable,[3] figures it is possible to compile
a table showing the growth in the populations of the Welsh counties
between 1700 and 1801 (Table I, Fig. 2).

TABLE I

Population growth in the counties of Wales, 1700–1801
(Source: *Census 1801, Census 1821*)

Counties	1700	1750	1801	Percentage increase	
				1700–50	*1750–1801*
Anglesey	22,800	26,900	33,806	18·0	25·7
Brecknock	27,200	29,400	31,633	8·1	7·6
Cardigan	25,300	32,000	42,956	26·5	34·2
Carmarthen	49,700	62,000	67,317	24·7	8·6
Caernarvon	24,800	36,200	41,521	45·8	14·6
Denbigh	39,700	46,900	60,352	18·2	28·7
Flint	19,500	29,700	39,622	52·2	33·4
Glamorgan	49,700	55,200	71,525	11·1	29·5
Merioneth	23,800	30,900	29,506	29·8	—3·4
Monmouth	39,700	40,600	45,582	2·3	12·2
Montgomery	27,400	39,000	47,978	35·1	29·5
Pembroke	41,300	44,800	56,280	8·4	25·6
Radnor	15,300	19,200	19,050	25·5	—0·8
Wales	406,200	490,800	587,128	20·9	19·6
England	5,068,800	5,977,100	8,285,852	17·9	38·8

[1] *Census 1821*, xxxiv; *Census 1841*, 34–8.
[2] See discussion, D. Williams, 'A note on the population of Wales, 1536–1801',
Bulletin of the Board of Celtic Studies, 8 (1935–37), 359–63; G. T. Griffith, op. cit.,
4–13.
[3] G. T. Griffith, 'Rickman's second series of eighteenth century population figures',
Journal of the Royal Statistical Society, 92 (1929), 260–2.

The steady growth of population in Wales through the seventeenth century[1] is shown by Table I to have continued into the eighteenth. Between 1700 and 1750 the relative increase in numbers was, on average, greater than that in England. This increase, of course, did not occur equally in all counties. In Flintshire over the period, population grew by over one-half, but in Monmouthshire there was hardly any change. Of the seven counties in which numbers increased by more than the average, the changes in Caernarvonshire, Flintshire, and Montgomeryshire were the most spectacular, while at the other end of the scale the counties of Brecknock, Monmouth, and Pembroke increased least.

In the second half of the century, on the other hand, when there was a very great increase in the total population of England, the growth for Wales as a whole remained much the same as it had done in the early part of the century. But again this average figure obscures many detailed differences. As in the previous period seven counties had more than average increases in population, but only three of these, Cardiganshire, Flintshire, and Montgomeryshire, had also increased more than the average in the period 1700–50; a continuity probably due to the steady development of lead and copper mining, the smelting industries, and the woollen industries respectively. Neither Glamorgan nor Monmouthshire had great increases in population in the second half of the century. It is true that the iron industry was expanding at such centres as Cyfarthfa and Ebbw Vale, but it was not until coal mining developed more fully in the nineteenth century that the great population increases associated with the two counties took place.[2] Two counties, Merioneth and Radnorshire, had fewer people in 1801 than estimated for 1750. However rough the estimates for the earlier date, it must be concluded that, in addition to the emigrants who went mainly to the United States, many people must have left these dominantly rural areas for the growing industrial centres, either in Wales or in England. These population movements were not new, but they were intensified at the turn of the century.

Much has been written about the reasons for the population changes at this time, and the relative importance of an increasing

---

[1] L. Owen, 'The population of Wales in the sixteenth and seventeenth centuries', *Transactions of the Honourable Society of Cymmrodorion* (1959), 99–113.
[2] W. Rees, *An historical atlas of Wales* (Cardiff, 1951), plate 70 (*a*).

birth-rate and a decreasing death-rate.[1] It is safe to say that generally the most important single factor which led to the growth of population was the increasing survival of children of the first few years after birth; a result partly of a better and more secure food supply, but mainly of real advances in medical knowledge and a growing awareness of the need for personal and public hygiene. These general trends were not necessarily reflected in all parts of the country, and south-west Wales has already been noted as an area which did not conform.[2] From the information available it is impossible to say precisely to what extent the rate of population growth in any particular area was influenced by migration. But it is clear from East's maps of population in 1700 and 1801[3] that as well as a great increase in total numbers there was, during the eighteenth century, a great distributional change. In 1700 the most densely populated counties lay in an east-west belt stretching from the Home Counties to Gloucestershire. At the eastern and western ends of the belt stood the two major sea ports of the time, London and Bristol. Outside the belt, population density was low. In Wales no county had a population density of more than 100 per square mile and in mid and west Wales, excluding Anglesey and Pembrokeshire, population density was less than 50 per square mile. By 1801 this pattern had been radically altered and the axis of population was north-west – south-east. London maintained its dominance in the south but the rapidly expanding industrial regions of the Midlands and the north-west superseded all other areas. Buer argues that to explain the growth of urban areas in terms of rural-urban movement is hazardous,[4] yet in most growing cities deaths exceeded births in the second half of the eighteenth century. Considerable migration from the countryside must have taken place and must have been an important element in this demographic change.

[1] E.g. G. T. Griffith (1926), op. cit., 27–44; T. H. Marshall, 'The population problems during the industrial revolution', *Economic Journal Supplement* (*Economic History*), 1 (1929), 429–56; H. J. Habakkuk, 'English population in the eighteenth century', *Economic History Review*, 2nd series, 6 (1953–54), 117–33; T. McKeown and R. G. Brown, 'Medical evidence related to English population changes in the eighteenth century', *Population Studies*, 9 (1955–56), 119–41; for a detailed study of the processes of population growth see J. D. Chambers, 'Population change in a provincial town: Nottingham 1700–1800', in L. S. Pressnell (ed.), *Studies in the industrial revolution* (London, 1960), 97–124.

[2] D. Williams, *The Rebecca riots* (Cardiff, 1955), 90–5.

[3] In H. C. Darby (ed.), *An historical geography of England before A.D. 1800* (Cambridge, 1948), 524–5.

[4] M. C. Buer, *Health, wealth and population in the early days of the industrial revolution* (London, 1926), 74–5.

Judged by the scale of movement in the country as a whole Wales was little affected by population changes. Over the century four counties only, those of Anglesey, Cardigan, Caernarvon, and Flint, changed their density categories on East's maps. This does not contradict the evidence of Table I, since both are derived from the same source, but it stresses the point that although many of the percentage changes shown in the table are large, they are based upon numbers of people which are very small in comparison with the county areas. Changes in Welsh population must therefore be viewed against the wider background of the greater relative, and far greater absolute, changes which were taking place in England at the same time. The process involved, of course, was the same and the effects in Wales the same as in England, albeit on a smaller scale. By the turn of the century population was increasing rapidly and people were becoming concentrated in the areas of expanding industry; manufacturing regions which owed their size partly to natural increase but which also grew at the expense of the poorer rural areas. At a time when there were more mouths to feed, a decreasing proportion of the population was engaged in agricultural activities.

Improvements in communications, which did so much to promote rapid industrial development in the second half of the eighteenth century, also had important effects upon agriculture. Coastwise and river traffic had for centuries provided routes for the carriage of agricultural produce. The coastal areas of much of south and west Wales were linked with Bristol, which acted as a main port and market. Liverpool, though less important, supplied the same needs for north Wales. Mid Wales was served by one of the most important of Britain's river arteries, the Severn, and Welshpool, near the head of navigation, had developed as a meeting place for packhorse and wagon routes. The construction of canals greatly improved the transport of goods by water and by the end of the eighteenth century efficient, though limited, waterway links existed between some of the lowland agricultural areas and either the manufacturing centres or the major ports.[1] But it was upon the roads that most agricultural produce was carried and here transport was less effective. There were three traditional east-west routeways across Wales: the south

[1] H. C. Darby, op. cit., 515; C. Hadfield, *The canals of south Wales and the border* (Cardiff, 1960), *passim.*

Wales coast road, the Usk–Tywi route, and the north Wales coast road. These had always been used for through traffic to Ireland and had rarely served or influenced the country through which they

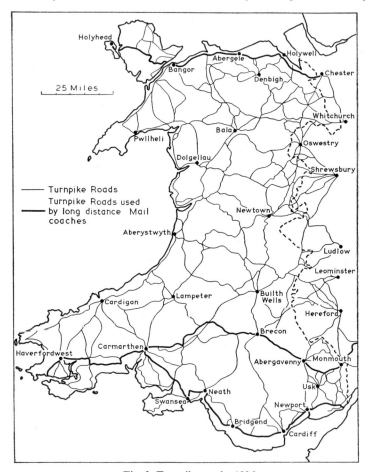

Fig. 3. Turnpike roads, 1806

(Source: J. Cary, *Traveller's companion, or a delineation of the turnpike roads of England and Wales* (London, 1806).)

passed. It was not until after 1750 when the turnpike trusts became active that Wales developed a road network which compared in any way with the system it had under the Romans. The surfacing would not have satisfied modern or Roman standards, for the influence of Telford and Macadam had not yet been felt, but most writers at the turn of the eighteenth century compared the turnpike roads favourably with parochial by-roads, which were very poor.[1] Turn-pike roads never formed more than a small proportion of the total road system but they did provide quicker trade links than Wales had ever possessed and were vital to agricultural development, although within forty years they were to be the foci of rioting in rural areas.

Fig. 3 shows the turnpike roads in Wales just after the turn of the century and also the approach roads from the major borderland towns. In addition to the traditional through-routes to Ireland, which still carried long distance coach traffic and which had gained in importance following the union of England and Ireland in 1800, there was quite a widespread network. These roads served not only to promote trade, but also as channels along which all the economic, political, and social forces penetrated and influenced Wales at this time. Proximity to good roads meant much more than accessibility to markets; it meant a real link with conditions in lowland England. On purely deductive grounds the influence of the forces should diminish in two directions. First, there should be a decrease with distance from a road, and secondly, there should be a decrease east to west, as the barrier formed by the Welsh massif (Fig. 4) emphasized the effects of distance.

Less closely tied to the communication network than other aspects of farming was the trade in cattle, which grew in importance as the eighteenth century proceeded. Herds of black cattle and also of sheep were driven from convenient collecting points to the expanding markets of London and the Midlands, as far as possible avoiding the main routeways and towns. Many thousands of beasts were driven out of Wales each year. The best animals were usually selected for sale and this effectively prevented widespread improve-ments in the stock. Though the cattle trade itself was not directly dependent upon transport it was, as much as any other branch of farming, ripe for the reforms which followed upon the improvement in communications.

Such then were the closely interrelated forces at work upon the agricultural landscape during the Napoleonic wars. In this chapter the aim has been to provide a general statement of what they were

[1] E.g. J. Fox, *General view of . . . Glamorgan* (London, 1796), 51.

and the ways in which they generally operated. It is only by examining material such as that described in the next chapter that the detailed working of such powerful forces of change in limited areas can be seen.

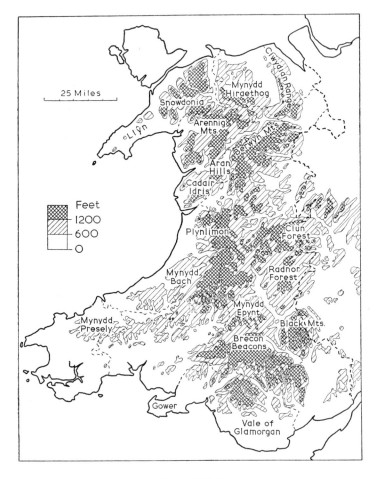

Fig. 4. Relief

CHAPTER 2

THE COLLECTION OF INFORMATION

DESPITE pleas by John Graunt in 1676 that particulars of crops and livestock be compiled to facilitate relief in case harvests should fail,[1] no detailed agricultural surveys on a country-wide scale were attempted until the latter half of the eighteenth century. A number of incomplete surveys and rough estimates were available, such as those of Edward Lhuyd[2] and Gregory King[3] made in the closing decade of the seventeenth century, but as time passed the lack of fresh, systematic information was gradually felt. Between 1750 and 1775 pamphleteers focused attention upon the need for enquiries,[4] and surveys began to be made. Arthur Young was the pioneer in this field. The record of his observations while on a journey from Suffolk to South Wales was published in 1768[5] and was the first of a large number of agricultural surveys by him. In 1778 William Marshall began publishing his commentaries upon agricultural conditions,[6] and six years later the *Annals of Agriculture* first appeared. Thereafter the making of surveys gained momentum so that for the period of the Napoleonic wars a great deal of information is available, though it varies considerably in form and accuracy. Broadly speaking, the material is either statistical, cartographic or literary in nature, and will be studied under these headings.

Statistical evidence

The statistical surveys of the period really begin with the work of Sir John Sinclair in Scotland. In 1790, with the support of the General

[1] C. H. Hull (ed.), *The economic writings of Sir William Petty* (Cambridge, 1899), II, 396.

[2] See F. V. Emery, 'English regional studies from Aubrey to Defoe', *Geographical Journal*, 124 (1958), 315–25; idem., 'A map of Edward Lhuyd's "*Parochial queries in order to a geographical dictionary, etc.*, of Wales (1696)" ', *Transactions of the Honourable Society of Cymmrodorion* (1958), 41–53.

[3] G. King, *Natural and political observations and conclusions upon the state and condition of England* (London, 1696), Section 7: reprinted in G. E. Barnett (ed.), *Two tracts by Gregory King* (Baltimore, 1936).

[4] E.g. Anon., *A compendium of the corn trade* (London, 1757), 25; Anon., *Sentiments of a corn factor on the present situation of the corn trade* (London, 1758), 23–4; W. Pennington, *Reflections on the various advantages resulting from the draining, inclosing and allotting of large commons and common fields* (London, 1769), 47–8; W. Donaldson, *Agriculture considered as a moral and political duty* (London, 1775), 172–4.

[5] A. Young, *A six week's tour through the southern counties of England and Wales* (London, 1768).

[6] W. Marshall, *Minutes of agriculture* (London, 1778).

3

Assembly of the Church in Scotland, he began a survey based upon a schedule of one hundred and sixty queries which he circulated to all parish ministers.[1] Information under the four heads of geography and natural history, population, production, and miscellaneous was required. The results were published in his *Statistical account of Scotland*,[2] but proved to be more descriptive than statistical.

Minchinton has described how similar methods, though on a far less comprehensive scale at first, were adopted by the Home Office; enquiries which were given urgency by harvest failures and the threat of invasion.[3] In 1795 the Secretary of State for Home Affairs circularized the lords lieutenant of the counties of England and Wales asking for statistical details of the harvest. In particular, a comparison was sought between the harvest of 1795 and that of the previous year.[4] The request for information was generally forwarded by the lord lieutenant to local magistrates who actually made the returns.[5] The replies varied in format, in the amount and in the type of information which they contained, for the questions asked were imprecise. For some counties, such as Lancashire and Gloucestershire, there are a great many returns; for others, such as Montgomeryshire, it is clear that one return was meant to represent the whole county. For a number of counties no returns at all exist. Of the counties of Wales seven are represented either in whole or part, but only Glamorgan has more than one return (Fig. 5).

In 1798 the threat of invasion brought about the taking of what have come to be known as the 'Lieutenancy Records'. The government planned, if invasion took place, to destroy all crops and stock in coastal areas. Agricultural statistics were thus collected for coastal parishes in the south of the country so that the losses would be known, and these were sent to the Home Office.[6] As far as is known none exists, or indeed was ever compiled, for Wales.

The failure of the harvest of 1799, another poor harvest in 1800, and the rapidly rising price of grain prompted the government to circularize the bishops for information. This time the scope of the enquiry was much more limited and consequently the replies were

---

[1] A. M'Callum, 'Sir John Sinclair', *Scottish Journal of Agriculture*, 19 (1936), 218.

[2] Sir J. Sinclair, *Statistical account of Scotland*, 20 vols. (Edinburgh, 1791–98).

[3] W. E. Minchinton, 'Agricultural returns and the government during the Napoleonic wars', *Agricultural History Review*, 1 (1953), 29–43.

[4] P.R.O., H.O.42, 36.

[5] P.R.O., H.O.42, 36–7.

[6] P.R.O., H.O.42, 39.

more standardized.[1] Four categories of information were required: yields of various crops at the last harvest, the local price of various agricultural products in 1798, 1799 and 1800, the amount of the

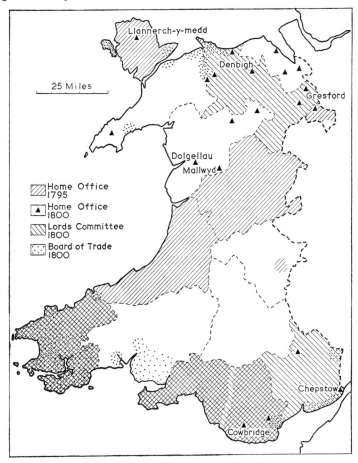

Fig. 5. Government surveys, 1795–1800

(SOURCE: P.R.O., H.O.42, 36–7, 52–5; B.T.6,139. 'Second report of the Lords' Committee on the dearth of provisions', *Parliamentary Papers*, 2 (1800–1), 25–76.)

previous harvest yet unconsumed, and the extent to which foreign grain was imported or wheat substitutes used. The questions were sent by the bishops to selected clergymen. In some dioceses, such

[1] P.R.O., H.O.42, 52–5.

as Chester and York, the model questions from the Home Secretary were incorporated into a printed form which provided spaces for the incumbent's answers. The Bishop of Chester also circulated a printed letter in which he explained the reasons for the enquiry.[1] When completed, the returns were collected by the bishops and sent to the Home Office. For some dioceses very many of these returns are extant; Chester, York and Lancaster are particularly outstanding in this respect. For Wales the coverage is not nearly as good. The returns for eleven parishes in the diocese of St. Asaph are available, seven transmitted by the bishop and four, from outlying parishes, sent direct to the Home Office,[2] and for three Welsh parishes in the diocese of Chester. The three remaining Welsh dioceses contributed only six further replies. The counties of Brecknock, Cardigan, Carmarthen, Montgomery, Pembroke, and Radnor are unrepresented (Fig. 5). Although the returns of 1800 are an improvement upon those of 1795 both in the amount and quality of the information which they yield, they lack uniformity and provide a thin and uneven coverage.

The scarcity of food and the imminence of social disquiet caused grave concern and in the following year the government again collected agricultural statistics, the well-known Acreage Returns. As before, the Home Secretary enlisted the aid of the bishops, whose officers distributed the specially printed forms to all parishes, with instructions that they should be returned direct to the Home Office.[3] The original blank form was printed in London. Together with space for the insertion of the name of the parish and diocese it provided a column for the return of the acreages occupied in the cultivation of wheat, barley, oats, potatoes, peas, beans, and turnips or rape, and also a very generous space for general remarks (see frontispiece). The decision to call for returns of rye acreages must have been taken later, for the crop was entered in manuscript on many forms. In some dioceses, such as St. David's and Lichfield and Coventry, the forms were reprinted locally, presumably because there were not enough to complete the circulation, and these have 'rye' printed as the second item in the crop list. Apart from the crop statistics, many of the forms include the remarks of the incumbent. Quite a number of

---

[1] P.R.O., H.O.42, 52.
[2] Letter from the Bishop of St. Asaph to the Duke of Portland (9 Nov. 1800), P.R.O., H.O.42, 53.
[3] P.R.O., H.O.67.

these are formal affirmations of accuracy, and others appeals to the Secretary of State for some personal favour or for the redress of a grievance. The curate of Bridstow, Herefordshire, complained bitterly about the stipend he received,[1] the vicar of Newchurch, Monmouthshire, pleaded for promotion for his son in the army,[2] while the incumbent of Ystradgynlais, Brecknockshire, thundered against the increasing riches of the industrialist.[3] Many others, however, supply commentaries of rural conditions which are both interesting and informative. The forms for Ciliau Aeron, Cardiganshire,[4] and Llandysul, Montgomeryshire,[5] give very enlightening reasons for the high barley acreages returned for those parishes; in the one barley was the bread corn, and in the other it was intended for the distilleries. The form for Bosbury, Herefordshire, records the existence of common arable fields worked on a three-year system, which occupied half the cropped land in the parish.[6]

The coverage provided by the returns of 1801 is by no means complete.[7] The random scatter of the missing parishes in most areas suggests that neglect by the bishops' officers to distribute the forms was not a major factor in determining the unrepresented areas. In the few instances where whole counties are without returns neighbouring counties within the same diocese are normally well covered.[8] The diocese of Peterborough is the only one for which no returns are available, but even here, covering notes from the incumbents show clearly that the forms were received, and some, at least, completed and returned to the Home Office.[9] The incomplete coverage must therefore be attributed either to the failure of the incumbents to reply or to the subsequent loss of the forms.

For Wales, returns for roughly 60 per cent of the parishes are extant. Fig. 6, which compares by hundreds the areas of parishes for which returns exist with the areas of those not returned, shows that the coverage is very uneven. Anglesey is completely without

[1] P.R.O., H.O.67, 12.
[2] P.R.O., H.O.67, 13.
[3] P.R.O., H.O.67, 22.
[4] P.R.O., H.O.67, 22.
[5] P.R.O., H.O.67, 21.
[6] P.R.O., H.O.67, 12.
[7] H. C. K. Henderson, 'Agriculture in England and Wales in 1801', *Geographical Journal*, 118 (1952), 339.
[8] D. Williams, 'The Acreage Returns of 1801 for Wales', *Bulletin of the Board of Celtic Studies*, 14 (1950–52), 55.
[9] H. C. K. Henderson, op. cit., 339.

record, while for Caernarvonshire the only return is for one detached parish well within the boundary of Denbighshire. Two of the hundreds outside this north-eastern area are also without returns:

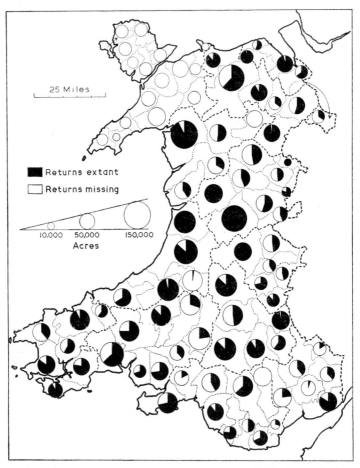

Fig. 6. Acreage Returns, 1801: parish coverage available, by hundreds
(SOURCE: P.R.O., H.O.67, 1, 6, 12–13, 21–2.)

Edeyrnion in Merioneth, and Caerphilly in Glamorgan. Several other hundreds are very poorly covered: Penarth, Cardiganshire, Llangyfelach, Glamorgan, and Skenfrith and Usk, Monmouthshire. Other parts of Wales are well represented, especially that part of central Wales where the four adjoining hundreds of Genau'r-glyn,

Cardiganshire, Machynlleth and Llanidloes, Montgomeryshire, and Rhayader, Radnorshire, have complete records. Incompleteness of coverage is obviously a disadvantage, for where large areas are without returns, as in north-west Wales, they must be excluded completely in any analysis of the 1801 figures. Where missing parishes are well scattered among those which have returns, and this is the more usual situation, no major difficulty arises. What is perhaps most unfortunate is that in certain areas where sharp and interesting differences in land-use might reasonably be expected, such as between the 'bro' and 'blaenau' of Glamorgan, the absence of data masks these contrasts.

It is clear then that for the period at the turn of the century Home Office papers provide a series of statistical enquiries which improved both in quality and coverage with each new survey. The returns of 1795 vary greatly in the material which they provide and are very general in nature, one short account often covering a whole county. The Lieutenancy Records of 1798 refer only to the coastal areas of southern England and so are outside the scope of this work. The returns of 1800 are based upon standardized questions and are easier to use for comparisons in area. The format is more uniform than that of 1795 but still there are wide variations in the data returned. Although the returns refer to parishes, they provide an unsatisfactory sample of the total number. The 1801 returns are the last of the series and by far the most useful. The limited scope of the enquiry meant that each incumbent understood exactly what was required, while the use of printed forms enables direct comparisons to be made. The method of distributing the forms to each parish ensured that, with the exception of a few extra-parochial places, the whole country was covered by the survey. The Acreage Returns thus form an important element in any examination of agricultural conditions during the Napoleonic wars.

Another important statistical source is the Census. The redistribution of people during the eighteenth century led to a violent controversy between those who believed the population of Britain to be decreasing and those who thought it was increasing. Both views caused concern; the first because it suggested that Britain's power as a nation was diminishing and the second because it was held that an increase in population inevitably brought increase in poverty, particularly in a period of scarcity, a point of view which the publication of Malthus' *An essay on the principles of population* in 1798 emphasized. It was against this background that the need for enumeration was felt, and the Population Act of 1800 was passed without opposition. In the following year a schedule of six questions was circulated. In England and Wales the responsibility for answering was divided between the overseer of the poor and the incumbent of each parish, both of whom received their forms from the High Constable.[1] The first question asked for the number of inhabited houses, the number of families occupying them, and the number of houses uninhabited. The second asked for the return of the total population of each parish, and for separate male and female totals. The third question attempted a different type of classification of total population; into three broad occupation categories. Those employed in agriculture were to be distinguished from those employed in trade, manufacturing, and handicraft, while a third category was intended for all those not returned under the first two. The collection of these statistics was the responsibility of the Poor Law overseer. The fourth and fifth questions were answered by the incumbent and are of less direct value. They were concerned with the return of baptisms, marriages, and burials compiled from the parish registers for selected years between 1700 and 1800. The last question was a general one which allowed further remarks or explanations to be made. Both the *Enumeration abstract* for England and Wales, containing the returns from the overseers of the poor, and the *Parish register abstract* appeared in 1802, and in these figures are given for all the parishes, hundreds, and counties of Wales. The Census of 1801 provides a very valuable statistical complement to the Acreage Returns of the same year.

Ten years later the second Census of Great Britain was taken. Its organization was not greatly different from that adopted in 1801 but two important changes were made in the questions circulated. First, the returning officer was asked, when enumerating uninhabited houses, to distinguish between those being built and those uninhabited for any other reason. Secondly, in the classification according to occupation, information was required about the number of families engaged in the various activities, instead of the number of persons.

[1] *Guides to official sources, No. 2, Census reports of Great Britain 1801–1931* (H.M.S.O., London, 1951), 12.

Several other less important statistical sources relate to Wales at this period. In 1800 the Lords' Committee on the dearth of provisions was set up to examine the yield of the harvest of that year.[1] Evidence was taken from 'respectable and well-informed persons in different counties'. The results of the enquiry were tabulated by counties and published in an appendix to the report.[2] Details of seven crops are shown: wheat, barley, oats, rye, peas, beans, and potatoes. For each of these crops which was grown in the county the yield per acre in 1800 is given together with the proportion of an average crop which this figure represented. For some English counties four individual reports were recorded. For Wales, tables for the four counties of Denbigh, Glamorgan, Monmouth, and Pembroke appear, each consisting of one report only (Fig. 5).

In the same year the Board of Trade carried out a series of enquiries. In one of these, the Corn Returns,[3] local customs officers estimated what proportion of a normal crop the harvest of 1800 had yielded, commented on the state of the grain at threshing, and reckoned the stocks of the previous harvest remaining. Details of the same seven crops as in the Lords' Committee enquiry were given together with information about the hay crop. Many coastal areas of Wales have returns but by no means all coastal districts are represented. The coasts of north Cardiganshire, Merioneth, and Flintshire provide the greatest gap in the coverage (Fig. 5). Again the replies are fairly standardized in form but statistically they are imprecise.

In the *Annals of Agriculture*, edited by Arthur Young, material of two kinds throws light upon agriculture during the Napoleonic wars. First, there is general information in the form of a series of tables showing the average monthly prices of wheat, barley, oats, and beans for each county from the beginning of the wars until the end of 1805.[4] The price of beans, little grown in Wales at this period, frequently does not appear for the Welsh counties and occasionally the prices of other crops are missing. The figures for Anglesey particularly suffer from omissions. Secondly, there are the more detailed replies to circular letters distributed by Arthur Young,

[1] *Parliamentary History*, 35, cols. 832–54.
[2] 'Second report of the Lords' Committee on the dearth of provisions',. *Parliamentary Papers*, 2 (1800–1), 25–76.
[3] P.R.O., B.T.6, 139.
[4] *Annals of Agriculture*, 19 (1793)–44 (1805).

which contain a certain amount of statistical material. Again the evidence for Wales is less satisfactory than that for England. To some of the questionnaire surveys there are no replies from Wales; where there are replies they are limited both in number and in their detail. The Welsh returns fall into three groups according to their dates of transmission: 1795, 1799–1800, and 1804–08.

In 1795 Arthur Young, apprehensive about reports of food shortages, circularized his correspondents asking for details of grain stocks, the prices of agricultural provisions, and the methods being employed to relieve scarcity and the distressed poor. The sparseness of the material on Wales may be judged from the fact that of the seventy-nine answers, only two were from Wales; one from Anglesey and one from south Cardiganshire.[1] Later in the year and after the harvest the continuing shortages prompted Young to make a second investigation very much like the first. This time questions relating to the yield of the harvest, agricultural prices and wages, and the poor were asked. To this circular there was only one reply from Wales, again from Anglesey[2] (Fig. 7).

For nearly four years no letter from Wales containing statistics was printed in *Annals of Agriculture* but in 1799 and 1800 six replies to queries by Young appeared. The first, from Denbighshire, was in answer to a questionnaire dealing mainly with a proposed method of extinguishing tithes, but to which there was an addendum on agricultural prices.[3] Two more, from north Cardiganshire and Monmouthshire, were in reply to a circular letter seeking information on the effects of the severe frost and backward spring of 1799, especially upon agricultural prices.[4] Late in that year the same two correspondents supplied further particulars of crop prices and the state of the poor.[5] Early in 1800 a report on the distress caused among the poor by the scarcity of provisions came from the extreme south of Cardiganshire.[6] (Fig. 7).

The returns of 1804–08 were less concerned with agricultural prices than those to the earlier queries of Arthur Young. Four replies, one each from the counties of Brecknock, Cardigan, Monmouth, and Pembroke, dealt with the causes and effects of the wheat

[1] Ibid., 24 (1795), 42–3, 260–6.
[2] Ibid., 25 (1796), 344–5; 26 (1796), 11–12.
[3] Ibid., 32 (1799), 275–8; 33 (1799), 98–102.
[4] Ibid., 33 (1799), 129–31, 147–50, 199–203.
[5] Ibid., 34 (1800), 162–5.
[6] Ibid., 35 (1800), 5–8.

mildew which had damaged the crop of 1804.[1] An exchange of letters between Young and his correspondent in north Cardiganshire produced information on the improvement of the upland wastes[2]

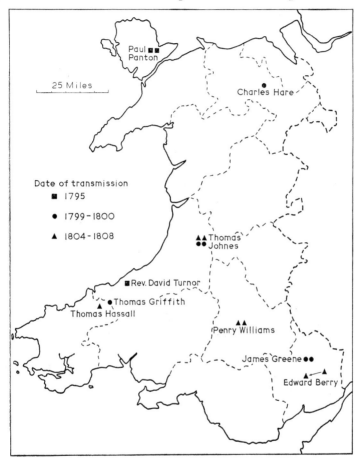

Fig. 7. Replies to questionnaire surveys by Arthur Young, 1795–1808
(SOURCE: *Annals of Agriculture*, 24 (1795) – 45 (1808).)

while two further reports from Brecknockshire and Monmouthshire supplied details of the relationship between corn growing and the activity of the distillers[3] (Fig. 7).

[1] Ibid., 43 (1805), 321–3, 506–7; 44 (1806), 156–8, 161.
[2] Ibid., 43 (1805), 577–83.
[3] Ibid., 45 (1808), 513–7, 556–8.

A number of other surveys, all undertaken in the year 1800, are now lost or destroyed. Early in the year the Board of Agriculture circularized over one hundred of the chief magistrates of the major towns in Britain and also seventy-one of its principal correspondents asking for details of corn prices and the methods in use for relieving the poor.[1] Another survey enquired about the prospects for the harvest and a brief report by the president, derived from the replies of 'noblemen, clergymen, and magistrates', was sent to the Board of Trade.[2] Such was the government's desire for information that yet another series of investigations was being carried out by the Board of Taxes upon instructions from the Treasury. A survey of the harvest and of grain stocks was made late in October 1800, and seems to have been disturbing enough to lead very quickly to a second enquiry, in November, into local self-sufficiency in grain and the use of substitutes.[3] The urgency of the investigation was impressed upon the tax receivers and surveyors who made the returns. It is unfortunate that none of this material can now be traced.

The returns of acreages under hops in England and Wales, which first appeared for the year 1807,[4] are more important in a negative than in a positive way. As none of the statistical sources mentioned so far accounted for hops these excise figures provide additional material. The major producing centres for hops were all in England but the returns are useful because they confirm the general absence of the crop in Wales. The nearest major centre of production lay in north-east Herefordshire. In only a few Welsh parishes on the outer fringes of this area, where river valleys carried tongues of lowland westwards, were hops grown. In all parishes the acreages shown are small.

It is clear that the statistical material discussed above is varied in the information it provides and in its detail. For study it may conveniently be divided into three categories. For the period 1795–1808 there are a number of minor, fragmentary sources: the surveys of

[1] *Copy letter book Sept. 1793–Oct. 1800* (Jan. 1800), Board of Agriculture manuscripts, Royal Agricultural Society of England, London.

[2] Letter from Dundas to Lord Liverpool (2 July 1800), P.R.O., B.T.1, 18.

[3] Letters from George Rose to Board of Taxes (22, 23 Oct. and 17 Nov. 1800), *Treasury letter copy book, No. 1*, Board of Inland Revenue Repository, Hayes, Middlesex.

[4] 'An account of the total number of acres of land in Great Britain under the cultivation of hops', *Parliamentary Papers*, 17 (1821), 345–70.

Arthur Young in 1795, 1799–1800, and 1804–08, the Home Office surveys of 1795 and 1800, and the surveys of the Lords' Committee and Board of Trade, both of 1800. These are discussed in Chapter 3. Secondly, there are the Acreage Returns of 1801, to which Chapters 4 and 5 have been devoted. Thirdly, studied in Chapter 6, are the Censuses of 1801 and 1811.

Cartographic evidence

Maps also fall into three major categories. There are the maps which resulted from the work of the Ordnance Survey, the estate and farm plans which frequently were drawn under the patronage of the larger landowners, and the maps which normally accompanied enclosure awards.

In 1791 the scheme for a general survey of the country which had been under the guidance of the Royal Society was adopted officially and the Ordnance Survey created. This was partly a result of the death in the previous year of General Roy, the leading advocate of a national survey, who had directed much of the field work to that date and whose loss, it was feared, was more than an unofficial body could sustain, but more important was the pressing need to produce reliable maps for use in the threatened war with France.[1] Consequently the first accurate mapping of the British Isles was begun. The first edition was preceded by the *Surveyors' Drawings*, which are available for southern England, the Midlands, and Wales.[2] Most of this area, including the whole of Wales, was mapped on the scale of two inches to one mile, but limited parts of southern England were covered on the scales of three inches or six inches to one mile. Maps were produced not on the sheet lines of the first edition but for irregularly shaped areas bounded by rivers or roads. The first of these to be drawn for Wales was in the Pembroke–Tenby area, which was surveyed in 1809. The whole of the south Wales coast was completed before 1815 and by 1820 the counties of Pembroke, Carmarthen, Glamorgan, and Monmouth had been surveyed together with the greater parts of Anglesey, Caernarvon, Merioneth, Denbigh, Brecknock, Radnor, south Cardigan, and south-east Montgomery. Progress after this period was rather slow and the mapping of Flintshire, south-east Denbighshire, north Cardiganshire, and north Montgomeryshire was completed between

[1] Sir C. Close, *The early years of the Ordnance Survey* (Chatham, 1926), 29.
[2] The original manuscripts are now held in the Map Room, British Museum.

1830 and 1835. No key exists to the series, but it is clear that the standard symbols of the later editions were employed. Rivers, roads, buildings, woodland, orchards, parkland, and rough pasture are shown, and sometimes field boundaries are inserted. On some sheets hachuring or hill-shading indicates relief and on others marshland is represented, but these symbols do not seem to have been used uniformly in each area. While many printed maps appeared in this period none gives as detailed and comprehensive a picture of the Welsh landscape as these manuscript drawings of the Ordnance Survey.

Estate and farm plans are not nearly as numerous for this period as they are for the middle of the nineteenth century, when the larger-scale plans of the Ordnance Survey and the Tithe Redemption Commission provided a stimulus to detailed mapping. What maps are available generally depict land which was owned by one of the bigger landowners and in this sense they may not be altogether typical. Some examples exist for Wales in which large continuous tracts are shown. More often, as one might expect, the maps represent fragmented estates and sometimes fragmented holdings. Field and farm boundaries and the farm buildings are nearly always shown, but scales and accuracy of drawing vary greatly from one map to another. Occasionally broad land-use categories are represented and it is possible to distinguish arable, meadow and pasture, woodland, and rough pasture. On a very few maps the crops grown in each field appear. Most of these estate plans have now passed, with other estate documents, into the keeping of larger libraries and record offices.

Gonner has described how five main methods were employed to enclose commons and to extinguish common rights.[1] Of these, only one, enclosure by act of parliament, is of concern here. Parliamentary enclosure was not only the method most widely used at the turn of the century but also that in which the officially appointed commissioners of enclosure were responsible for drawing up formal awards and maps.[2] The acts usually directed that one copy of the award and accompanying map should be deposited either in one of the central courts of Justice at Westminster, or with the Clerk of the

---

[1] E. C. K. Gonner, *Common land and inclosure* (London, 1912), 43–70.
[2] M. W. Beresford, 'Commissioners of enclosure', *Economic History Review*, 15 (1946), 130–40.

Peace for the county, and another copy should be left in the keeping of the parish incumbent and churchwardens. The General Enclosure Act of 1801,[1] which standardized the procedures already in use, confirmed the practice. Awards and maps deposited in the central Courts of Justice are now generally held in the Public Record Office. The documents deposited in other places tend to have become dispersed since that time. Some are in county record offices or in the collections of large libraries, others have passed into private hands or are in the custody of local government authorities.

Wales was probably less affected by parliamentary enclosure during the Napoleonic wars than most other parts of Britain. There were still extensive stretches of unenclosed coastal bog and dune, some valley marshland used as common grazing, and a few other areas, such as those in coastal Cardiganshire and western Pembrokeshire, where open arable fields persisted, but over most of the lowlands enclosure had already taken place, often many centuries before.[2] The enclosure which did occur at this time was more typically on the upland fringes of the agricultural area,[3] where very large tracts were frequently involved, but a number of factors retarded unlimited enclosure. Upland moors were agriculturally marginal and productivity was low; the cost of enclosure, always considerable, was thus relatively high. Again, there was at times local opposition to the enclosure of the moorlands which had been the centres of ownership disputes for many years. Feeling was so sensitive at Llanddeiniolen, Caernarvonshire, and on Mynydd Bach, Cardiganshire, that rioting occurred,[4] but such disturbances were rare. The acreages of land enclosed by act in Wales have been tabulated in a number of *Parliamentary Papers*[5] but probably the best, though incomplete, list is that compiled by Bowen.[6] This

[1] 41 Geo. III, c. 109.

[2] See discussion, J. H. Clapham, *An economic history of modern Britain* (Cambridge, 1950), I, 25–7.

[3] E.g. J. G. Thomas, 'The distribution of the commons in part of Arwystli at the time of enclosure', *Montgomeryshire Collections*, 54 (1955), 27–33.

[4] A. H. Dodd, *The industrial revolution in north Wales* (Cardiff, 1933), 77–8; D. Williams, 'Rhyfel y Sais bach', *Ceredigion*, 2 (1952), 39–52.

[5] E.g. 'A return of all acts passed since the year 1800 for the inclosure of commons or waste lands in England and Wales', *Parliamentary Papers*, 48 (1843), 489–520; 'Appendices to the report of the Royal Commission on land in Wales and Monmouthshire', *Parliamentary Papers*, 33 (1896), 766–71.

[6] I. Bowen, *The great enclosures of common lands in Wales* (London, 1914), 47–56. More complete and accurate, though without acreages, is the list in T. I. J. Jones, *Acts of parliament concerning Wales, 1714–1901* (Cardiff, 1959), 276–99.

shows that between 1793 and 1815 acts were passed for Wales authorising the enclosure of over 200,000 acres (Fig. 8), which accounted for roughly one-eighth of the land then lying in common or waste.[1] The map does not show enclosure carried out by private agreement, of which little record remains. For north Wales a summary of enclosures, both parliamentary and by consent, between 1700 and 1845 has been compiled by Dodd.[2]

From the enclosure awards and maps it is normally possible to obtain information about three aspects of the landscape. First, old enclosures can be distinguished from those established by the act and hence the location of the old moorland edge or the limit of the common land is usually quite clear. Secondly, the apportionment of the common land is shown and, thirdly, enough information is normally given about the owners of the old farms to establish the post-enclosure ownership pattern. The allotments created by the enclosure commissioners were not necessarily immutable; sometimes plots of land were sold very quickly afterwards and sometimes the terms of the award were not strictly followed. Some of the new boundaries shown on the maps never actually existed on the ground, but generally the enclosure documents are an adequate guide to the evolution of the landscape at the time of parliamentary enclosure.[3]

Of the three types of manuscript maps available only one, the *Surveyors' Drawings*, gives a complete coverage of the whole country for the period under review. From this point of view the Ordnance Survey maps are the basic cartographic documents, but the information which they provide is limited. This can be amplified by use of the larger-scale plans which, though they depict limited, discontinuous areas, are far more detailed and can, if carefully chosen, be used as sample illustrations. The contrasting networks of farm and field boundaries and a more precise idea of the land-use patterns of the time emerge from the estate and farm plans, while the parliamentary enclosure maps show one of the chief means by which the rural landscape was changing. In Chapter 7 the *Surveyors' Drawings* and the estate and farm plans have been studied together; Chapter 8 has been devoted to enclosure award maps.

[1] I. Bowen, op. cit., 11.

[2] A. H. Dodd, 'The enclosure movement in north Wales', *Bulletin of the Board of Celtic Studies*, 3 (1925–27), 216–38.

[3] E.g. J. G. Thomas, 'Some enclosure patterns in central Wales', *Geography*, 42 (1957), 25–36.

Literary evidence

A great deal of contemporary writing relates to agriculture in Wales during the Napoleonic wars. There are two main sources from which information may be derived. The first is the material

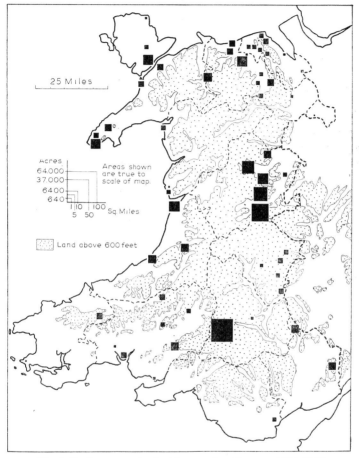

Fig. 8. Enclosures authorized by act of parliament, 1793–1815
(SOURCE: I. Bowen, *The great enclosures of common lands in Wales* (London, 1914).)

in the reports of the Board of Agriculture and Internal Improvement; the second is the commentary upon agriculture provided by the independent surveyors and travellers who produced the topographies, so popular at this period.

After his statistical survey of Scotland had been underway for three years, Sir John Sinclair was appointed first president of the newly founded Board of Agriculture, of which Arthur Young was secretary, and immediately attempted to collect agricultural information in England and Wales as he had done in Scotland.[1] His proposed appeal to the clergy had to be abandoned, however, under pressure from the Archbishop of Canterbury, who opposed any investigation which might revive the tithe controversy.[2] In place of the projected questionnaire survey itinerant surveyors were appointed to prepare reports on the state of agriculture in all the shires of England and Wales. The quarto reports for the six counties of north Wales were published together under the title *General view of the agriculture of north Wales* in 1794, and in the same year separate reports for the counties of Brecknock, Cardigan, Carmarthen, Monmouth, Pembroke, and Radnor also appeared. The report for Glamorgan followed in 1796. A preface to each report makes it clear that, although each was the result of an actual survey, the original reports were meant to be tentative, the intention being to re-publish the work after circulation for criticism in each county.[3] Interested persons were asked to write comments on the actual reports, especially wide margins being provided for the purpose, and to return them to the Board of Agriculture.

A great deal of additional material was collected by this means and shortly after a uniform plan was adopted for the consolidated octavo reports.[4] *General view of the agriculture and domestic economy of north Wales* appeared in 1810, the report for Monmouthshire in 1812, and the two volumes on south Wales in 1814. Different surveyors were generally appointed for the later reports and these frequently provide accounts quite separate from those of the earlier reports. This was so in Wales[5] where Walter Davies (usually known by his bardic pseudonym, Gwallter Mechain), the author of the north Wales and south Wales reports, had not written any of the earlier accounts. Hassall, the author of the Monmouthshire report, had previously written the accounts of Pembrokeshire and

---

[1] Sir J. Sinclair, *Account of the origin of the Board of Agriculture, and its progress for three years after its establishment* (London, 1796), Appendix F, 36, 38–46.

[2] J. M. Ramsey, 'The development of agricultural statistics', *Journal of Proceedings of the Agricultural Economics Society*, 6 (1940), 120.

[3] Sir J. Sinclair, op. cit., Appendix N, 70.

[4] Plan for reprinting the agricultural survey by the president of the Board of Agriculture, *Annals of Agriculture*, 24 (1795), 548–55.

[5] *Parliamentary Papers* (1896), op. cit., 572.

Carmarthenshire. Williams has pointed out that none of the authors of the octavo reports appeared to have made use of the Acreage Returns of 1801.[1] Indeed, no attempt seems to have been made by the Board of Agriculture surveyors to use any statistical or cartographic material other than that acquired during the course of each investigation. Two distinct word pictures of the agriculture of Wales at this time are thus available, the one covering the period immediately before the turn of the century (1794–96) and the other the period immediately after (1810–14).[2]

Over the three centuries before 1800 topographical writing grew steadily in popularity. With the improvement of roads, as the turnpike trusts increased in number, and the growth of a new literate and leisured middle class, the desire to explore the home country, or to read of the exploration of others, led to a great increase in the number of topographical works in the last quarter of the eighteenth century. Not only did numerous topographies become available, but some were so popular that they were reprinted many times. For example, the sixth edition of S. J. Pratt's lengthy *Gleanings through Wales, Holland, and Westphalia* was published within seven years of its first appearance in 1795. Some of the topographies, such as E. W. Brayley and J. Britton's *The beauties of England and Wales*, the volumes of which appeared between 1801 and 1815, attempted a complete description of a county, or of the whole country.[3] Frequently these relied heavily upon the accounts of earlier writers and sometimes large sections were copied word for word. Other works take the form of travel diaries and provide commentaries of the tour carried out by the author. R. Warner's *A walk through Wales in August, 1797* is such an account. Clearly, works of the second type refer only to the limited areas through which the authors travelled.

The description of agricultural conditions was rarely the main aim of the topographers, though sometimes a great deal of information is provided incidentally. What an author recorded was obviously

---

[1] D. Williams (1950–52), op. cit., 57.

[2] For the first systematic, geographical treatment of the Board of Agriculture reports, see W. G. East, 'Land utilization in England at the end of the eighteenth century', *Geographical Journal*, 89 (1937), 156–72.

[3] For a treatment of accounts of this type see G. E. Fussell, 'Agriculture and economic geography in the eighteenth century', *Geographical Journal*, 74 (1929), 170–8.

dictated by his personal inclination, but generally speaking antiquities and picturesque settings were the great magnets. Wales as a whole was well endowed with what the topographer sought, and a fairly large number of works are available. North Wales (especially Snowdonia), south Wales, and parts of the Wye valley, are well documented but mid Wales was generally not popular.

The differences between the two major written sources must be reflected in their interpretation. On the one hand, the Board of Agriculture reports were specifically concerned with agricultural conditions; they were standardized in form and the area with which each dealt was precise and fixed. It was only in the quality and detail of the material which they contained that the reports varied, some being the result of careful surveys and others little more than the edited comments of a few prominent landowners. On the other hand, the topographers were not specially concerned with agriculture, there was no standardized approach and both the area and material depended on the whim of the author. The quarto reports of the Board of Agriculture are considered in Chapter 9, the octavo reports in Chapter 10, and the topographies in Chapter 11.

In Chapter 1 the general economic, political, and social background to the period was described. This chapter has dealt with the statistical, cartographic, and literary material available. The remainder of the work is concerned with analysing these three types of evidence for Wales, partly to reconstruct a period picture but also to assess the influence of the forces of change, operating at this time, upon the agricultural landscape. Both these aims are of interest because in Wales not only do physical conditions differ widely from place to place, but physical accessibility, and consequently the impact of economic, political, and social stimuli from outside, is an important variable.

II. STATISTICAL EVIDENCE

CHAPTER 3

MINOR STATISTICAL SOURCES, 1795–1808

STATISTICAL returns in the period 1795–1808 are best viewed as introductory to the Acreage Returns and Census of 1801 and the Census of 1811. While the 1801 and 1811 surveys provide a reasonably complete and detailed picture, the minor sources are uneven in coverage and in content.

Arthur Young's surveys, 1795

The earliest of the surveys between 1795 and 1808 are those of Arthur Young. To the first of his circulars, early in 1795, there were two replies from Wales[1] (Fig. 7). From the first reply, that of Paul Panton, Plas-gwyn, near Pentraeth, it is evident that Anglesey, the traditional granary of Wales, was dominantly a barley producer. No rye and little wheat was grown. Usually enough grain was produced to provide a substantial export, but fears were expressed that, as a result of the drought of the previous summer and the severe frost and snow of the winter, the production in 1795 would not be enough for the island's needs. In his recapitulation of the survey Young brought together the statistics from each county and presented them in tables.[2] From these it is clear that the prices of provisions in Anglesey were below average, but so were wages. Of all the counties quoted the cost of labour in Anglesey was the lowest, at eleven pence a day; barely more than half that in Middlesex at the other end of the scale. The prices of wool, hay, straw, and coal were much more like the average for the country, which must have made these commodities seem extremely expensive in Anglesey. The outlook for 1796 was not good, and money was being collected in order to buy corn to sell at a reduced price to the poor. But corn was not the only commodity affected; the cost of mutton, beef, pork, and also potatoes was increasing.

In south Cardiganshire the position was not much different, according to the report of David Turnor.[3] Wheaten bread was not eaten, even by the 'substantial farmers', whose bread-corn was

---

[1] *Annals of Agriculture*, 24 (1795), 260–6; Young's questionnaire is reprinted in full in W. E. Minchinton, 'Agricultural returns and the government during the Napoleonic wars', *Agricultural History Review*, 1 (1953), 31–2.

[2] *Annals of Agriculture*, 24 (1795), 327–48.

[3] Co-author of the quarto report of the Board of Agriculture on Cardiganshire.

barley or oats. The lack of demand for wheat meant that its price had not risen. Though, generally speaking, the crops of barley and oats were not as good as usual, the dry, sunny summer of 1794 had produced high yields in the uplands, where grains flourished under such conditions. Good stocks of grain were thus reported at Cardigan and Newcastle Emlyn, and the prices of provisions were slightly lower than in Anglesey. The poor were not as numerous in south Cardiganshire as in other parts of the country but the failure of the potato crop, a very important element in the diet of the poor, seemed likely to bring further distress. Those who were not in full-time work were mostly maintained by the landlords, partly by advances of wages and partly by gifts.

To the second circular sent in October 1795, the reply from Panton, in Anglesey, seems to imply that conditions were not as bad as expected earlier in the year.[1] The barley crop had been better than in 1794, the oats crop average, and potatoes were particularly good. While there had been a slight increase in meat prices, the cost of most other foods had remained steady or decreased slightly. Wages, however, were now reported to be rising, much against the wishes of Panton who, though sympathetic with the plight of the poor, feared that, once increased, wages could not be reduced again if food prices fell.

Home Office survey, 1795

Also in October, the Home Office carried out the first of its enquiries,[2] the answers to which were compiled by the magistrates. Of the seven counties for which there are returns (Fig. 5), Glamorgan has two replies; one for the area to the east of the river Ogwr and one for the area to the west, but neither quotes detailed statistics. Anglesey, Cardiganshire, and Pembrokeshire each have one reply covering the whole county, but giving no more than general comparative statements. Flintshire, Montgomeryshire and Radnorshire only have returns which give statistics of crop yields in 1794 and 1795, but even so comparisons between the counties cannot easily be drawn. The Flintshire statistics refer to the four parishes of Hanmer, Overton, Worthenbury, and Bangor Is-coed, in the detached part of the county, for which the total produce in 1794 and 1795 of wheat, barley, oats, peas, and (for one parish) beans, is listed. The Montgomeryshire return purports to show average yields per acre over

---

[1] *Annals of Agriculture*, 26 (1796), 11–12.
[2] P.R.O., H.O.42, 36–7.

the whole county for the two years in question and for an average year. In addition to the five crops shown on the Flintshire form, rye is included. The Radnorshire return covers the borough of Radnor for 1794 and 1795; the quantity of wheat and barley produced by all landowners and tenants, fifty-five in all, is shown.

Some of the difficulties which arise when an attempt is made to use the results of unsystematic surveys of this kind emerge. Not only are there the problems of poor coverage and of comparisons between descriptive and statistical replies, but it is difficult to compare even the statistical returns. The Montgomeryshire return refers to the whole county and quotes average yield per acre. The Flintshire and Radnorshire returns refer to small areas within the counties and quote total produce yielded. Apart from the fact that crop acreages are not shown, so that conversions to a standard measure cannot be made, both the list of crops and the bushel measure used varied from county to county. Clearly then, only comparisons of the harvest of 1794 and 1795 within each county are possible, and for Wales as a whole the amount of useful material is severely limited.

The harvest of 1794 seems to have been below average, and that of 1795 generally worse. But a steady decrease in yield was not experienced for all crops. While the Radnorshire magistrates reported a fall of one-seventh in the quantity of both wheat and barley produced between 1794 and 1795, this was not so elsewhere. In all four Flintshire parishes the quantity of wheat produced fell but in none did that of barley fall. In a number of instances the produce of oats and peas increased. Of course, nothing is known of the acreages planted under each crop, but there is nothing to suggest that these altered greatly. Indeed, similar fluctuations in yield may be recognized in the descriptions of the harvests of Anglesey, Cardiganshire, and Glamorgan. The reasons for these differences are not clear, but undoubtedly the abnormal weather in the autumn and winter of 1794, mentioned by Young in his first circular, contributed towards crop failure. While there is uncertainty about the causes, the effects of the poor harvests were already being felt. In Cardiganshire corn prices had begun to rise.

Arthur Young's surveys, 1799–1800

For the three years after 1795 no statistical information was collected, but news of bad harvests and further rises in prices prompted a number of surveys, both private and official. As so often happened, Arthur Young was the first to take action, and from four different questionnaire surveys there resulted the six replies of 1799–1800 from Wales[1] (Fig. 7). The theme which dominates the letters is the high price of crops and provisions, and a number of views are advanced upon the causes and also upon the consequences of that state.

Writing from the upper part of the Vale of Clwyd in the spring of 1799, Charles Hare claimed that, with the exception of poultry, mutton, and butter, necessary articles were not only dearer, but of poorer quality than in most parts of England. This he attributed almost wholly to the method employed locally of auctioning and then sub-letting tithes, a system which increased the costs of farmers and also tended to retard agricultural improvement. His argument, however, may well be exaggerated as he seems to have suffered personally from tithe taking.

Later in the same year comparable reports came, on two occasions, from Thomas Johnes of Hafod, Cardiganshire, and James Greene, of Llansanffraid, Monmouthshire. The first letters were written before the harvest, and tell much the same story. The severe frost of the winter and the lateness of the spring had damaged many of the crops, turnips particularly, but the prospects for the corn harvest seemed good. In hilly parts there had been heavy losses of lambs and sheep; Johnes estimated that nearly one thousand of his had died. During the harsh weather the stocks of hay had become depleted, forcing up the price, and oats, potatoes, and chopped straw had been fed to livestock. The costs of provisions of all kinds had also increased, the only exception being that of coal in Llansanffraid, less than ten miles from the coalfield, where the price was roughly half that paid by Johnes for Lancashire coal. It is not surprising that the main fuel in north Cardiganshire was peat. In December 1799 further reports were supplied by Johnes and Greene. Around Hafod the corn harvest of oats, barley, and rye had been as good as expected, while potatoes and turnips were not successful. In north-west Monmouthshire farmers had not been as fortunate. The wheat crop yielded about half the average and, though the production of barley and oats was satisfactory, its quality was low. The high prices with which the year began eased

---

[1] *Annals of Agriculture,* 33 (1799), 98–102, 147–50, 199–203; 34 (1800), 162–5; 35 (1800), 5–8.

slightly following the harvest, but not sufficiently to bring any great comfort to the poor, who suffered most from these increased costs. Both Johnes and Greene described how relief was given to the poor. In the district around Hafod the poor were no more numerous than usual. The lead mines offered an alternative source of employment, but all those who wished were engaged by Johnes for such work as stone wall-building and the digging of sheep out of snow-drifts in winter. In north-west Monmouthshire it was unusual for farmers to discharge their labourers in hard weather, when farm work could not be undertaken, but those who did become unemployed found work easily in nearby iron works, which always required more hands. No plan had been adopted for supplying the poor with food at reduced prices, but farmers often sold grain to their labourers at well below the market price and at Abergavenny soup kitchens had been set up. In south Cardiganshire, on the other hand, a report sent by Thomas Griffith, in March 1800, makes it clear that the lack of alternative employment had distressed those already poor and also had contributed towards the large numbers unemployed. Corn was in short supply, stocks were not expected to last beyond the month of May, and little remained of the potato harvest. An association of landowners and the more prosperous farmers had therefore been formed and was actively devising means of preventing famine. Members of parliament had been petitioned to stop all malting, farmers were urged to bring corn to market regularly and to sell it in small quantities, and £2,000 had been collected so that barley and potatoes could be imported.

Home Office survey, 1800

In the Home Office investigation of 1800 the four standard questions produced replies from the clergy which are more amenable to comparison than those to its earlier survey even if, for Wales, the coverage provided is little better[1] (Fig. 5). The first question asked for the yield of the harvest and for comparisons with other years, but despite the fact that six crops were specifically mentioned and yield per acre was asked for, there is considerable variation in the form of the replies. From most it appears that the harvest of 1800 was well below average; only in Chepstow, Dolgellau, and Llanrwst was it thought normal. The reply for Mold is typical of those which included statistics. The 1800 yield in bushels per acre for wheat

[1] P.R.O., H.O.42, 52-4.

was 15, for barley, 13, for oats, 20, and for potatoes, 50. This compared with average yields of 20, 30, 30, and 160 bushels per acre respectively.

Fortunately a particularly detailed return was made for Bangor Is-coed, Flintshire, which includes statistics comparable with those returned in 1795. Thus for 1794–95 and 1798–1800 the annual produce of wheat, barley, oats, and peas is available in bushels of 38 quarts. For the later period the acreages under each crop and the yield per acre were also returned. If 1799 is taken as a base year for comparative purposes, and there is much to suggest that it was a year in which the harvest was appreciably below average,[1] then the leanness of some of the harvests in other years is illustrated. The produce of wheat in 1799 was 3,988 bushels. In 1800 it was 3,227 bushels, in 1794, 3,065 bushels, and in 1795, 2,068 bushels. The figures for oats tell the same story, while those for barley and peas demonstrate even more impressively how bad were the harvests in the middle 1790's. The produce of barley in 1794 was little over one-half that of 1799, and the produce of peas, one-eighth that of 1799. There may have been small changes in the acreages under each crop during the six years, as there were between 1798 and 1800, but they cannot have accounted for these great variations in amounts produced.

The very poor harvests of the period contributed towards the situation revealed by the second question put to the clergy. This asked for a comparison between the prices of agricultural commodities in October 1800 with prices in 1798 and 1799. As might be expected, answers were far more precise than those to the first question; there might have been doubt about the estimation of average yields or total produce, but market price was well known. Price trends in all parishes were remarkably consistent and therefore it will be sufficient to consider four sample parishes: Gresford, Denbighshire, in the north-east, Llannerch-y-medd, Anglesey, in the north-west, Mallwyd, Merioneth, in north-central Wales, and Chepstow, Monmouthshire, in the south-east. Unfortunately, no return exists for the south-west (Fig. 5). While the prices at Gresford and Llannerch-y-medd markets were quoted in terms of Winchester measure, in Mallwyd the 80-quart hobet was used and in Chepstow different measures were used for different crops, both a 10- and

---

[1] E.g. *Commercial and Agricultural Magazine*, 1 (1799), 217–8.

15-gallon bushel being employed. Clearly this difficulty can be resolved by expressing crop prices in each parish as a percentage of the 1798 price, and this has been represented graphically in Fig. 9, where Windsor market prices have been included in each diagram for comparison. Admittedly this is a crude technique because it relies so much on the supposition that 1798 prices are comparable from parish to parish, but even so it can be seen that, as at Windsor, wheat prices in Wales doubled over two years.

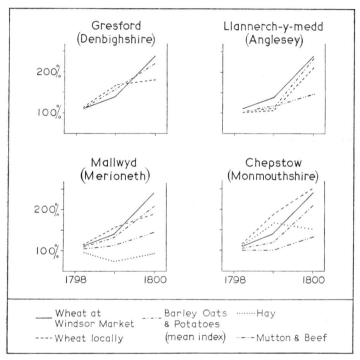

Fig. 9. Price trends of agricultural products, in selected parishes, 1798–1800; prices expressed as percentages of those in 1798
(SOURCE: P.R.O., H.O.42, 54; *Census 1831.*)

If, by a proportional calculation, actual wheat prices for 1798 are so expressed that they refer to Winchester quarters, the measure used at Windsor, then Welsh prices are seen in perspective. The Windsor wheat price of £3 0s. 9d. a quarter was matched by the Gresford price of £3 and the Chepstow price of £2 17s. 6d. Further to the west wheat prices were lower. In Llannerch-y-medd a Winchester bushel would have cost £2 2s. 0d., and in Mallwyd, £1 14s. 0d. In 1800 the incumbent of Cowbridge, Glamorgan, claimed that the price of wheat in his market was 'lower than in any other part of the kingdom'. Though it was comparatively low for that year, at £4 16s. 0d. per Winchester quarter, the 1800 price in both Llannerch-y-medd and Mallwyd were lower. Although in relative terms the inflation in wheat prices affected Wales fairly uniformly, wheat prices themselves were by no means uniform over the country. In the border shires prices were comparable with those at Windsor, but westwards they were considerably lower.

The prices of barley, oats, and potatoes were also affected by the inflation (Fig. 9). Whereas in England the prices of these crops rose less sharply than that of wheat, in Wales, especially in central and western parts, the reverse was more often true. It is noticeable also that there was no marked fall in prices westwards, as for wheat. The prices of the three crops in mountainous areas were, in one or two instances, higher than in the borderland, and frequently higher than the average for England and Wales.[1] Many of the returns stress that in the Vale of Clwyd, and in central and west Wales, barley, oats, and potatoes were the major food crops, and not wheat, which was 'very little grown or made use of'. The greater demand for barley, oats, and potatoes was the probable reason for the excessively high prices in these areas.

It is interesting to note how closely this description of conditions corresponds with that provided by Arthur Young. It is wholly consistent with his questionnaire survey of 1799–1800 and is firmly corroborated by the monthly corn prices printed in *Annals of Agriculture*. In Fig. 10 these statistics have been presented in summary form. A graph shows the trend of the average prices of wheat, oats, and barley in England and Wales from the beginning of the wars until the end of 1805, after which time monthly statistics were not published. Three distribution maps compare the prices of the major grain crops in the Welsh counties with the national average price in March 1801, at the peak of the wartime inflation. Though the highest prices were reached five months after the Home Office returns were made, the map of wheat (Fig. 10 *b*) still shows clearly

---

[1] 'An account of the grain of all sorts . . . in each year from January 5th, 1800, to January 5th, 1825', *Parliamentary Papers*, 20 (1825), 234–61.

the decline in prices westwards. The map of barley (Fig. 10 *d*), on the other hand, is impressive evidence of the great demand for that crop in Wales. In only one county, Pembroke, were prices below the average for England and Wales, and in two counties, Brecknock and Flint, prices were 30 per cent higher than the national average.

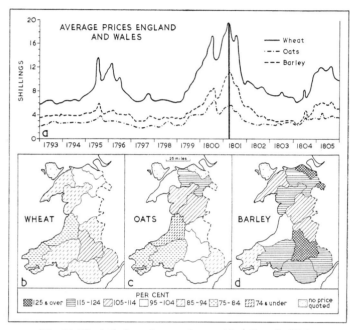

Fig. 10. The inflation of corn prices and its effects in Wales

a. Average monthly prices per Winchester bushel in England and Wales of wheat, oats and barley; January 1793–December 1805

b. Wheat prices in the Welsh counties expressed as a percentage of the average for England and Wales in March 1801, at the peak of the inflation

c. Oats prices in the Welsh counties expressed as a percentage of the average for England and Wales in March 1801, at the peak of the inflation

d. Barley prices in the Welsh counties expressed as a percentage of the average for England and Wales in March 1801, at the peak of the inflation

(SOURCE: *Annals of Agriculture*, 19 (1793) – 44 (1805).)

Of the other commodities included in the second question of the Home Office survey, information is scant. Beans and turnips were frequently not grown but a number of incumbents returned information about the price of hay, mutton, and beef. The graphs for

Llannerch-y-medd, Mallwyd, and Chepstow (Fig. 9) are typical. The price of hay changed very little; in some parishes it rose slightly as at Chepstow, in others it fell, as at Mallwyd. Meat prices generally increased, but not nearly as sharply as the grain and potato prices.

The third, fourth, and (for the four parishes of south-east Wales) the fifth questions were all closely related in that they dealt with the deficiency of grain, the methods used to alleviate the deficiency and the causes of the high grain prices. Without exception, all parishes reported that at the harvest of 1800 stocks of grain were low or had been completely used. With no surplus grain the effects of the poor harvest of 1800 were bound to be intensified, and to require urgent remedy. In Holywell, Flintshire, rice was mixed with wheat for bread-making, but despite the publicity given to rice as a substitute for the usual cereal[1] the practice does not seem to have been widely adopted. In most parishes shortages were relieved by the import of grain. In parts of north-east Wales, particularly in the Vale of Clwyd, barley was the major import, coming generally from the port of Liverpool. Between the harvests of 1799 and 1800, 3,000 bushels of barley were received in the parish of Mold, Flintshire, the equivalent of the produce in that year of 230 acres. In central and western parts of the country rye was the grain most needed, and in Dolgellau half the rye consumed had been imported by sea, mainly from London and Liverpool. In south Wales, a greater amount of wheat and flour was received, and the Chepstow supplies, at least, came through the port of Bristol.

From the Home Office survey of 1800, the best of the pre-1801 statistical enquiries, a picture of agricultural conditions in Wales at this time begins to emerge. A succession of very poor harvests between 1794 and 1800 had depleted the stocks of grain and led to local shortages in the staple crops. Prices rose markedly, especially that of the local bread corn, and in order to ease the deficiency imports were required on a considerable scale. But, as Figs. 9 and 10 demonstrate, these imports did little to arrest the inflation which had begun so dramatically and which was, over the next year, to become even more spectacular.

---

[1] E.g. 'Rice bread', *Annals of Agriculture*, 25 (1796), 535–7; 'On rice bread', ibid., 34 (1800), 440–4.

Lords' Committee survey, 1800

In the same year a number of other investigations were being carried out with roughly the same aim as the Home Office enquiry, and these provide supplementary information. The Lords' Committee investigating the dearth of provisions received reports from four Welsh counties,[1] three of which were in south Wales (Fig. 5). For Monmouthshire the evidence reveals that the produce of the 1800 harvest was well below average for all crops returned except peas, and that had it not been for the importation of grain, stocks would have been exhausted. In Glamorgan, although the three major grain crops were said to have produced an average harvest, at least one-third of the grain needed was imported. Like many other counties which were becoming industrialized,[2] it seldom produced enough for its own needs. In Pembrokeshire, also, the harvest had been poor. Stocks of wheat were low, but surprisingly there was plenty of barley, although the harvest in that crop was said to have yielded only half the average. The report to the Lords' Committee from Denbighshire corroborates the results of the Home Office survey. The crop deficiencies shown for the 1800 harvest parallel closely those returned by the incumbents of Gresford and Denbigh, and again the shortage of barley particularly was noted. Such was the dependence upon barley in Denbighshire that even when wheat was available, it was of little value, unless it could be mixed with barley for bread making.

Board of Trade survey, 1800

Essentially the Board of Trade Corn Returns of 1800[3] sought the same information as the other surveys of that year; it is remarkable how alike in form all the official investigations were. Each survey attempted to assess the yield of the 1800 harvest, each compared this with yields in an average year and each estimated the quantity of grain in stock. From what is known of the investigations of the Board of Agriculture and the Board of Taxes, these, too, asked for similar information. The Board of Trade enquiry is particularly valuable because it covers so many areas, particularly those in south-west Wales, which were not returned in the other surveys of 1800 (Fig. 5).

[1] 'Second report of the Lords' Committee on the dearth of provisions', *Parliamentary Papers*, 2 (1800-1), 25-76.

[2] G. E. Fussell and C. Goodman, 'Traffic in farm produce in eighteenth-century England', *Agricultural History*, 12 (1938), 359-60, 364.

[3] P.R.O., B.T.6, 139.

The return for Monmouthshire refers to the coastal districts between Newport and Chepstow, and also to a small area around Monmouth. Both in its physical features and in its historical development the Caldicot Level of coastal Monmouthshire is a distinctive region,[1] but at this period it was very little different from other parts of the county. The Corn Return is very similar to the Lords' Committee and the Home Office evidence, with crop yields well below average and less than a week's supply of grain available at the harvest. Only the hay crop was average, but the yield of oats was not as far below normal as elsewhere in the county. Around Cardiff the harvest was a little better, the wheat crop being reported as average. Consequently stocks were greater and a fortnight's supply of grain was in hand, although it is not made clear if this included imported grain. Certainly wheat yields were better than at Cowbridge, where the incumbent had reported to the Home Office that the crop was a third below normal, but in both areas potatoes had yielded only one-quarter of an average crop and the barley crop had failed. Further west, in coastal Carmarthenshire, there was no grain in stock at the harvest, although, here again, there was an average wheat crop. All other crops, except hay, were poor.

For Pembrokeshire there are three Corn Returns. The first refers to the peninsular hundred of Castellmartin to the south of Milford Haven, the second covers the hundred of Rhos immediately to the north of the Haven and including Haverfordwest, while the third is a combined report of conditions in the two hundreds of Dewsland and Dungleddy, which cover the area immediately to the south of Mynydd Presely (Figs. 4, 5). In Castellmartin, as in all other areas of Pembrokeshire, stocks were low, but generally the harvest had not been too bad. Peas and hay were abundant, oats produced an average crop, and the wheat and barley crops were not much below normal. Only the potato harvest failed completely. The hundred of Rhos was much the same, with grain yield very little below the average, and potatoes the only failure. In Dewsland and Dungleddy, which lay largely to the north of the traditional regional division between north and south Pembrokeshire,[2] the picture was

[1] See Sir J. F. Rees (ed.), *The Cardiff Region, a Survey* (Cardiff, 1960), 131; M. Davies, 'Common lands in south-east Monmouthshire', *Transactions of the Cardiff Naturalists' Society*, 85 (1955–56), 5–15; D. Sylvester, 'The common fields of the coastlands of Gwent', *Agricultural History Review*, 6 (1958), 9–26.

[2] See E. G. Bowen (ed.), *Wales, a physical, historical and regional geography* (London, 1957), 342–3.

very different. The crop yields returned were exactly the same as those given in the Lord's Committee enquiry, but there were no stocks of barley. Wheat, oats, and especially barley, were poor, and the only other food crop, potatoes, yielded one-quarter of the average. The year 1800 must have been a particularly hard one for the largely rural population of north Pembrokeshire.

For the coastlands of Cardigan Bay there is little evidence. In the extreme south details of a small area around the town of Cardigan were returned, and here no wheat was grown. Of the other crops, barley yielded well, except on the heavier soils, but all others were poor. Around Pwllheli, at the northern end of the bay, the harvest had been better with average crops of the three major grains and a deficiency in potatoes alone. In fact, the returns for north-west Wales as a whole suggest that here the harvest was better than in many other parts. The return for Bangor is the only one in Wales which described the crops of grain as better than average, and that for Holyhead, showing average crops, estimated that grain supplies sufficient for between a week and a fortnight were in hand. Further east, in the Vale of Conway and along the Denbighshire coast, harvests were much more like those in the rest of Wales. Wheat and oats yields were poor and the barley and potato crops failed.

The Board of Trade survey of 1800 provides, from its very nature, a biased account of agricultural conditions in Wales. It was compiled by customs officers who described what they saw in their own localities, which were coastal and nearly always lowland; there is no evidence of conditions in inland and upland areas. But when the Board of Trade survey is studied in conjunction with the Home Office and the Lord's Committee surveys then, as Fig. 5 shows, a far more representative coverage for the year 1800 results.

Arthur Young's surveys, 1804–1808

The last of the minor statistical sources of information on Wales during the Napoleonic wars is again a result of Young's efforts. Between 1804 and 1808 replies were transmitted to a number of his questionnaire surveys[1] (Fig. 7), but the fall in prices after March 1801 (Fig. 10), a result partly of the better harvests, made strictly statistical enquiries less urgent.

---

[1] *Annals of Agriculture*, 43 (1805), 506–7, 577–9, 581–3; 44 (1806), 156–8, 161; 45 (1808), 516–7, 556–8.

The fairly widespread mildew of the wheat crop of 1804 was the stimulus to one of the surveys. Wheat losses seem to have been general on most of the heavy valley lands, judging by the four returns from Wales. Penry Williams, of Pen-pont, Brecknockshire, reported the experiences of two farmers in his county and concluded that the yield was only half the average. Johnes, from north Cardiganshire, estimated the wheat harvest as not more than two-fifths the average. A poor crop was reported by Edward Berry of Llangofen, Monmouthshire, while Thomas Hassall of north Pembrokeshire wrote that a good sample of wheat was rarely seen and that only a third of the usual crop had been collected. Though wheat prices rose after the harvest no great distress was felt in Wales. As Johnes made clear in an earlier exchange of letters with Young, the harvest in 1804 of oats, barley, and potatoes, the principal foodstuffs over much of Wales, was good.

In April 1808 two further letters came from Penry Williams and Edward Berry, now at Llancaeo, near Usk, in reply to a query on the stopping of distilleries, a subject then being examined by a committee of the House of Commons. As farmers on quite a large scale both were strongly opposed to any proposal which would diminish the demand, and consequently the price, of barley. In Monmouthshire one-fifth of the tillage was under barley, and Berry argued that a fall in price would destroy the whole basis of turnip and barley husbandry and hence the progress of agricultural reform.

If all the minor statistical surveys of the period 1795–1808 which relate to Wales are considered, while there is by no means a complete coverage, information exists for all counties. It is also fortunate that, however fragmentary and unsatisfactory the replies to the enquiries, most of the surveys attempted to elicit the same type of information about the harvest. Again, there is little reason to suspect the accuracy of the replies; indeed there is a surprising degree of unanimity between the reports of Young's correspondents, the magistrates, the clergy, 'the respectable and well-informed persons', and the customs officials. It is true that some of the statistical evidence is contradicted by the views of contemporary English visitors to Wales. De Quincey, for example, commenting upon his stay in Merioneth in 1802, declared that the prices of provisions were far lower in Wales than in England.[1] But it is likely that such

[1] T. De Quincey, *The confessions of an English opium eater* (Everyman edn., London, 1907), 130–1.

judgements were based upon experience of the needs of English agricultural communities, rather than the very different needs in Wales. Certainly wheat was cheap in Merioneth, as the evidence of all four Home Office returns for the county shows, but this does not mean that the cost of living was low because barley and oats were far more important elements in the diet. As De Quincey himself admitted, 'the insipid white-grey bread of the towns' was not eaten in the county.

The statistical material of 1795-1808, in a summary, though accurate way, sets the scene for the far more detailed returns of 1801 and 1811. From this point of view alone it is valuable. It is of additional value because it gives details of crop yields, prices, and stocks, information rarely provided by the major sources, which were concerned principally with crop acreage and population.

CHAPTER 4

THE ACREAGE RETURNS OF 1801: CROP DISTRIBUTIONS

Problems of interpretation

WHEN in 1801, under instructions from the Home Office, the clergy in Wales attempted to collect details of the acreages devoted to the various crops in their districts,[1] they encountered difficulties. Some farms had never been properly measured and some were inaccessible, but more serious was the reluctance of farmers to give information. The incumbent of Newent, a Gloucestershire parish not far from the Welsh border, described the attitude of the typical farmer in his parish: 'He is apprehensive that the Government might compel him to bring corn to market at an unprofitable season, that his landlord may raise his rent, his parson call for a higher composition for tithes, the overseer assess him more to his poor rates, the highway surveyor advance him in proportion'.[2] In Wales a survey made by the officers of the established Church was particularly resented. The incumbent of St. Asaph writes: 'Farmers will not give any information to be depended upon, and the clergy should be the last people to put the question; they are already too obnoxious to them'.[3] Many incumbents therefore suspected that the acreages supplied by the farmers were less than they should have been, though few had any idea of the amount of the understatement.

The reliability of the returns was also criticised in the following year by the Board of Agriculture which reported: 'It appears to this committee that the returns transmitted by the Right Honourable Lord Pelham, as far as the members can ascertain by their personal knowledge of particular parishes, are so extremely erroneous as well as defective that they cannot safely be relied upon in forming any general conclusions respecting the quantities of land sown with

---

[1] P.R.O., H.O.67. For a transcription of the material for Wales see: D. Williams, 'The Acreage Returns of 1801 for Wales', *Bulletin of the Board of Celtic Studies*, 14 (1950–52), 54–68, 139–54; D. Thomas, 'The Acreage Returns of 1801 for Wales, an addendum', *Bulletin of the Board of Celtic Studies*, 17 (1956–58), 50–2.

[2] P.R.O., H.O.67, 11.

[3] P.R.O., H.O.67, 21.

any species of grain'.[1] The Board's judgement seems harsh, especially as it was based not upon detailed checking in the field, but upon the general impressions of those members who were present at the meeting. Again, it should be remembered that the Board was not a disinterested body. A similar survey which it had sponsored a few years earlier had to be abandoned under pressure from the Church, and hence some hostility towards the collection of agricultural information by the Secretary of State through ecclesiastical channels might be expected. But at the time the opinion of the Board prevailed. Such was the lack of confidence in the crop figures that they were not used by the government, but were promptly shelved.

Since 1948 a number of authors have used the returns to illustrate cropping during the Napoleonic wars. Some have been satisfied with their accuracy[2] while others have suggested that understatement of acreages exists.[3] These conflicting opinions, based upon uncertain evidence, are best resolved by comparing the Acreage Returns with other contemporary data. No comparable statistical material is available and literary evidence is imprecise. Fortunately, manuscript estate plans showing land-use provide a reliable means of testing the accuracy of the returns.

For fifteen, well-scattered parishes in Wales, manuscript estate plans cover areas which are sufficiently large and representative to provide good samples of the complete parishes.[4] From this material it is possible to estimate the arable acreage in each of the parishes at the turn of the eighteenth century. In Fig. 11 cropland acreages in 1801, derived from the Acreage Returns by adding together the acreages of the individual crops, have been related to the arable estimates, and it is clear that for most parishes there is a great discrepancy between the two values. Many difficulties arise in a comparison of this sort, but probably the greatest is that 'cropland' and 'arable' are not necessarily synonymous. Contemporary written evidence, such as the Board of Agriculture reports, establishes that in the parishes studied no important crops were omitted from the

[1] K. G. Davies and G. E. Fussell, 'Worcestershire in the Acreage Returns for 1801', *Transactions of the Worcestershire Archaeological Society*, 27 (1951), 18.

[2] E.g. W. G. Hoskins, 'The Liecestershire crop returns of 1801' (included in *Studies in Leicestershire agrarian history*), *Transactions of the Leicestershire Archaeological Society*, 24 (1948), 129.

[3] E.g. R. A. Pelham, 'The 1801 crop returns for Staffordshire in their geographical setting', *Collections for a History of Staffordshire* (1950–51), 233.

[4] D. Thomas, 'The Acreage Returns of 1801: a test of accuracy', *Bulletin of the Board of Celtic Studies*, 18 (1958–60), 379–83.

1801 survey, and thus the sum of the crop acreages represents total cropland. It is less certain what land marked as 'arable' on the manuscript estate plans actually comprised. In addition to cropland it certainly included bare fallow and may also have included rotation grassland, although at the height of the wartime grain shortages it is not likely that much potential arable was left in fallow or grass.

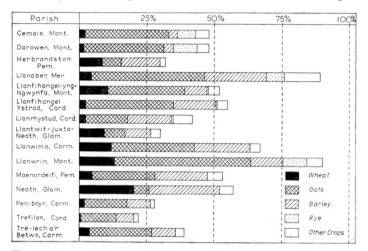

Fig. 11. Acreage Return cropland expressed as a percentage of estate plan arable estimates for fifteen Welsh parishes

(SOURCE: D. Thomas, *Bulletin of the Board of Celtic Studies*, 18 (1958–60), 379–83.)

The discrepancies shown in Fig. 11 between cropland returned in 1801 and the parish arable estimates are so great that it is difficult to see how any errors of calculation or interpretation could have caused them. It must be concluded first, that there was a considerable understatement of crop acreages when the 1801 survey was being made. On average over the fifteen parishes, cropland returned in 1801 was less than half that expected from the manuscript plan calculations. Secondly, the understatement varied from parish to parish, and presumably from farmer to farmer. In Llanaber, Merioneth, and Llanwrin, Montgomeryshire, the discrepancy was about 10 per cent, but in Pen-boyr, Carmarthenshire, and Trefilan, Cardiganshire, it was more than 70 per cent. Thirdly, it is clear that the variability in understatement was quite random in area. In Llanwinio, Carmarthenshire, the cropland returned was 67 per cent of the manuscript plan estimate, but for the adjacent parish of Tre-lech a'r Betws the figure was 39 per cent. These conclusions, when coupled with the incomplete coverage of the returns, present formidable problems in the interpretation of the material.

Two further, though less serious problems of interpretation should be mentioned here. The first arises from the rare occurrence of measurements in 'customary' or 'computed' acres. The sizes of these local measures varied widely from place to place, and sometimes, as in Glamorgan and Brecknockshire, three or more different measures were used in the same county.[1] The second is a more general point applicable to all parish data. Parish summaries, such as the Acreage Returns, give an impression of the average of actual conditions over the whole parish and may obscure marked differences over small areas. Variations in parish sizes will have the effect of changing the area over which the average is taken, and consequently the extent to which the differences within the parish will be obscured. In a region where parishes are small, cropping may appear far more diversified than in another region of large parishes; a result which might be due not to an actual difference but to parish sizes. The full implications of this have been considered by Coppock[2] and Weaver[3]; here it is sufficient to note that direct comparisons between areas where parishes are of widely differing sizes, such as between upland and lowland areas in Wales, should be drawn with caution.

Treatment of the data

Because of its nature the material derived from the Acreage Returns of 1801 requires special treatment. The incomplete coverage (Fig. 6) means that distribution maps, using parish boundaries as a framework within which to represent the intensity of cropping, have many blank spaces. These, if not misleading, certainly hinder interpretation. J. P. Dodd avoids the problem, supplying the missing details by informed guesswork, but the solution is not a happy one.[4] It seems better to consider the returns as a sample of the complete

[1] F. Seebohm, *Customary acres and their historical importance* (London, 1914), 100.

[2] J. T. Coppock, 'The relationship of farm and parish boundaries; a study in the use of agricultural statistics', *Geographical Studies*, 2 (1955), 12–26; idem., 'The parish as a geographical–statistical unit', *Tijdschrift voor Economische en Sociale Geografie*, 51 (1960), 317–26.

[3] J. C. Weaver, 'The county as a spatial average in agricultural geography', *Geographical Review*, 46 (1956), 536–65.

[4] J. P. Dodd, 'The state of agriculture in Shropshire, 1775–1825', *Transactions of the Shropshire Archaeological Society*, 55 (1954), 1–31.

distribution and employ a technique in which parishes without statistics are omitted altogether from the distribution maps.

The variable understatement of the acreages returned is less easy to overcome. Clearly a direct comparison cannot be made between the acreage devoted to cropland or to a single crop and the parish acreage, neither can direct comparisons be made between parishes, because apart from the fifteen parishes shown in Fig. 11 there is no means of knowing by how much acreages are deficient. Fortunately, as Pelham has pointed out,[1] the relative importance of the figures for the individual crops in any one parish seems approximately correct; an argument for which there is no conclusive proof but which is strongly supported by all distributional studies using the material. Farmers, bent upon deceiving their incumbents with fictitious acreages, most likely supplied figures which were understated, but consistent with the known cropping practices of the area. If they had not done so the deception would have been obvious. The method of treatment must, therefore, be based upon the relative importance of each crop within the parish; a parish wheat acreage, for example, cannot be accepted as an absolute value but can be studied in relation, say, to the barley acreage or the rye acreage or the total cropland of the same parish. While this does not eliminate the error completely, because not all farmers in a parish would have understated their acreages to the same extent, it does provide a less biased picture of actual conditions than any other method, and enables valid comparisons to be made between the relative importance of crops in different parishes.[2] It also has the merit of solving the difficulty caused by the use of customary acres. Provided the whole return was made in the local measure, no conversion to statute acres is needed as the standing of crops in any parish remains the same whatever measure was used.

Method of approach

The first attempt at the understanding of the statistics of 1801 is by an analysis of the distributions of the individual crops. Eight separate distribution maps have been prepared which show in turn the percentage of the cropland occupied by each crop (Figs. 12, 15, 16, 18–22). As crop distribution, unlike the distribution of rainfall

[1] R. A. Pelham, op. cit., 233.

[2] D. Thomas, 'The statistical and cartographic treatment of the Acreage Returns of 1801', *Geographical Studies*, 5 (1958), 15–25.

or height of ground above sea level, is not one of continuous gradation in which high values must pass through medium to low, a true isopleth map is inappropriate, especially when the statistics are on a parish basis. A dasymetric technique, such as that frequently used in population studies,[1] was therefore adopted. Unenclosed upland, land upon which no cropping took place, was outlined in a generalized way: on a map of this scale it is impossible to show either the intricacies of the moorland edge or the smaller moors. In the remaining areas of each map the percentage values derived from the returns were plotted over the major settlements of the parishes, and all those adjacent values which fell within one of a number of standard percentage categories were grouped together. The lines bounding these groupings[2] are not necessarily of constant numerical value, as are isopleths, but serve only to separate adjoining groupings. For the counties of Anglesey and Caernarvon there are no statistics, but for the remaining counties returns for over five hundred parishes provide ample material upon which to base a distribution map.

It should be stressed that the maps do not imply any relationship between the acreage under a crop and the size of the parish. For example, a high percentage of cropland under oats need not mean that a high proportion of the parish was devoted to that crop; a small part of the parish only may have been in cropland. There is good reason to believe that the importance of cropland varied greatly from place to place, especially between upland and lowland, and attention will be paid to these differences in a later chapter. With the exception of a very few parishes for which there is additional material, all that can justifiably be done with the distribution maps is to study the apportionment of the cropland between the various crops, irrespective of the importance of the cropland in any one parish.

Wheat (Fig. 12)

In a statistical study of the relationship between accumulated temperature, rainfall, and the yields of selected crops, Hooker[3] demonstrated a strong negative correlation between wheat yields

---

[1] E.g. J. K. Wright, 'A method of mapping densities of population', *Geographical Review*, 26 (1936), 103–10.
[2] The lines are normally termed *dasymetric lines*.
[3] R. H. Hooker, 'Correlation of weather and crops', *Journal of the Royal Statistical Society*, 70 (1907), 1–42.

and annual rainfall.[1] As rainfall increases so the quantity of wheat grown would be expected to decrease, especially on soils which maintain a high water content during winter months. In drier

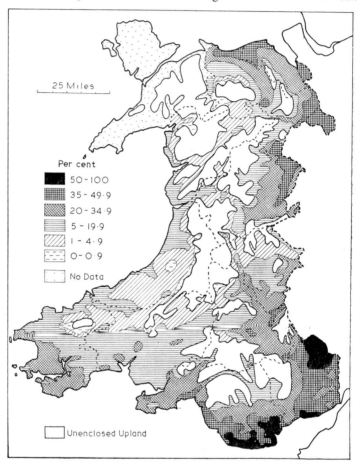

Fig. 12. Proportion of cropland in wheat, 1801
(SOURCE: P.R.O., H.O.67, 1, 6, 12–13, 21–2.)

areas the wheat plant's deep root system enables it to be drought-resistant and it is rarely affected by lack of rainfall in this country, except on excessively sandy soils. With these exceptions it is tolerant

[1] See also L. D. Stamp, *The land of Britain, its use and misuse* (London, 1948), 256.

of a wide range of soil conditions. One limiting factor is the length of the growing period which wheat requires—longer than any other crop returned in 1801.[1] Consequently, it is not suited to areas where

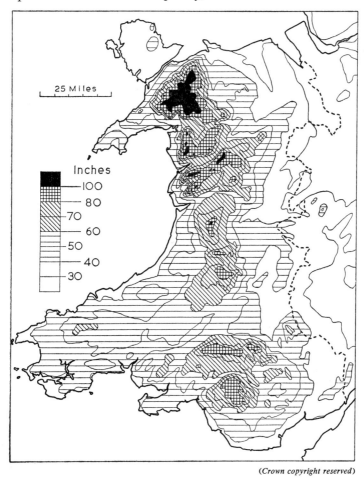

Fig. 13. Average annual rainfall, 1881–1915
(SOURCE: Ordnance Survey 1/625,000 series.)

spring is late. At a period when only autumn-sown varieties were available it was also most difficult to prepare land in time for seeding in these areas, for harvests tended to be retarded.

[1] K. H. W. Klages, *Ecological crop geography* (New York, 1949), 253.

Fig. 12 illustrates the extent to which the wheat plant's physical requirements influenced its distribution. A comparison first with the map of average annual rainfall (Fig. 13) shows how impressive was the inverse relationship between rainfall and wheat production, noted by Hooker. Along the north Wales coast where annual rainfall is 30 inches, over 35 per cent of the cropland was in wheat and in the Vale of Glamorgan, despite slightly greater rainfall, there were large areas where wheat occupied over 50 per cent of the cropland. Wheat decreased in importance westwards along the south Wales coast, and probably also along the north Wales coast, so that on the Cardigan Bay littoral less than 20 per cent of the cropland was under wheat, though annual rainfall is less than 40 inches. Even so, the contrast between the drier lowland areas and the moister uplands was still appreciable. In all those areas where annual rainfall exceeds 50 inches wheat was unimportant, sometimes occupying less than 1 per cent of the cropland.

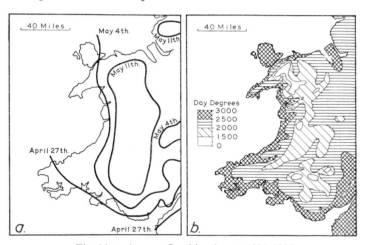

Fig. 14. *a*. Average floral isophenes, 1891–1925
(Source: J. E. Clark, I. D. Margary, and C. J. P. Cave, *Quarterly Journal of the Royal Meteorological Society*, 61 (1935), 238.)

b. Mean annual accumulated temperature, 1881–1915
(Source: S. Gregory, *Transaction and Papers, 1954*, Institute of British Geographers, 20 (1954), 65.)

A number of apparent anomalies in Fig. 12 are resolved when a study is made of some of the other physical requirements of wheat. For example, the Vale of Clwyd, which has annually less than 30 inches of rain, had a comparatively low proportion of cropland in wheat. This was almost certainly due to the nature of the soil. The Vale is a synclinal rift which is floored by a thick drift mantle containing a high proportion of Silurian fragments and masking all but a few Triassic outcrops. Soils, although rich, tend to maintain a high water table, especially in winter,[1] and seem to have discouraged further wheat growing. In areas such as lowland Brecknockshire, it is probable that the shorter growing season (Fig. 14 *a*, *b*) led to the lower wheat acreages. Although over 20 per cent of the cropland was in wheat, when compared with lowland Monmouthshire and the Vale of Glamorgan, the amount is small.

Considering the distribution as a whole, the areas where high proportions of cropland were in wheat are generally those which satisfy the plant's physical requirements best. But it is noticeable that from east to west values decrease, though not in a way which can be explained in terms of physical conditions. If anything, south Pembrokeshire is better suited to the production of wheat than the Vale of Glamorgan, but while the proportion of cropland devoted to wheat in Pembrokeshire nowhere exceeded 35 per cent, in Glamorgan it was frequently over 50 per cent. This problem is best postponed until an analysis can be made of crop rank.

Oats (Fig. 15)

Unlike wheat, oats mature early and are well adapted to growing in rainy districts where summer temperatures are rather low. But they are liable to fail in dry areas where high summer temperatures can cause them to ripen prematurely and produce thin, light grain. They are particularly unexacting in their soil requirements provided that the moisture content is reasonably high, and will produce well both upon light sandy soils in areas of medium or heavy rainfall, and upon lime deficient soils. Highest yields are obtained on heavy loams.

The ease with which oats thrive in moist, cool conditions is reflected strongly by Fig. 15; with a few exceptions, it is the converse of Fig. 12. It was the upland areas fringing the moorland which had the highest percentage of cropland in oats. While wheat frequently occupied less than 5 per cent of the cropland, more than 50 per cent was almost everywhere under oats, and in some districts, such as that around Bala, Merioneth, well over 75 per cent of the cropland was in oats, though, of course, the amount of cropland in these

---

[1] E. J. Howell, *North Wales* (The land of Britain), 41–3 (London, 1946), 634.

uplands was small (Fig. 36). In the lower areas of lighter rainfall the
percentage of the cropland under oats diminished, particularly along
the north and south Wales coasts and in the eastern-facing river

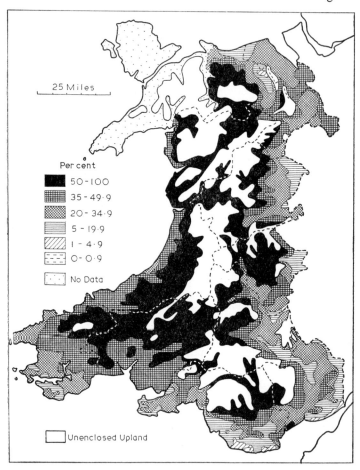

Fig. 15. Proportion of cropland in oats, 1801
(SOURCE: P.R.O., H.O.67, 1, 6, 12–13, 21–2.)

basins where, with annual rainfall below 40 inches (Fig. 13), the
crop occupied less than 20 per cent of the cropland over considerable
areas. As in the map showing the distribution of wheat there is
again a marked contrast between the wetter uplands and the drier
lowlands.

The wheat and the oats maps (Figs. 12, 15) do not show completely complementary density distributions and a number of areas provide important exceptions. In eastern Denbighshire and in the eastern parts of Flintshire both wheat and oats occupied over 35 per cent of the cropland. Earlier studies have shown that this area was the western fringe of the extensive wheat–oats region of the Cheshire Plain; a drift-covered area characterized by an intermixture of well-drained and extremely moist soils in which both wheat and oats could flourish.[1] In some other lowland areas the proportion of cropland under wheat and under oats was low. The most noticeable of these is the Vale of Clwyd in which less than 35 per cent of the cropland was in wheat, and less than 20 per cent in oats, but Gower and south Pembrokeshire also had low proportions of both crops.

The distribution shown in Fig. 15 is again broadly related to the physical requirements of the plant, especially its tolerance of a rainy climate. In all upland areas where conditions are too cold and wet, and the growing season too short to maintain high proportions of the cropland in wheat, oats were dominant but they also acted as a complement to wheat in at least one lowland area of very mixed drainage conditions.

Barley (Fig. 16)

That barley in some respects is ecologically akin to wheat is evident from its lowland distribution and Hooker, in his statistical study, was able to show a significant negative correlation between barley yields and summer rainfall.[2] But he also demonstrated a negative correlation with accumulated temperatures in the summer months, suggesting that the crop requires not only a dry, but also a cool growing period. The plant is outstanding for its ability to mature in a short growing season; much shorter than that normally needed for wheat. It is far more specific in its soil requirements. It demands better drainage than either wheat or oats and fares badly on heavy clays. It is particularly sensitive to mineral deficiencies and less tolerant of soil acidity than any other of the Acreage Return crops.

[1] D. Thomas, 'The Acreage Returns of 1801 for the Welsh Borderland', *Transactions and Papers, 1959,* Institute of British Geographers, 26 (1959), 169–83.

[2] R. H. Hooker, op. cit.

The map showing the distribution of barley (Fig. 16) like that of wheat shows marked contrasts over most of its area between lowland and upland, for upon both climatic and edaphic grounds the

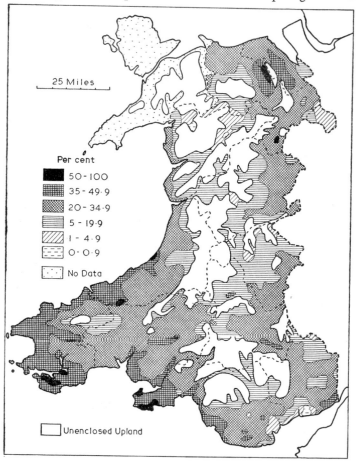

Fig. 16. Proportion of cropland in barley, 1801
(SOURCE: P.R.O., H.O.67, 1, 6, 12–13, 21–2.)

plant is less suited to higher land. In most lowland areas of light rainfall the crop was well represented, occupying generally more than 20 per cent of the cropland, and in some districts, particularly upon the non-acid soils developed from the Carboniferous Limestone in Gower and south Pembrokeshire (Fig 17), it occupied over

50 per cent of the cropland. In lowland areas of heavy soils the crop was excluded. In the zone fringing the Cheshire Plain, upon the wet coastal areas between Cardiff and Newport, and on the

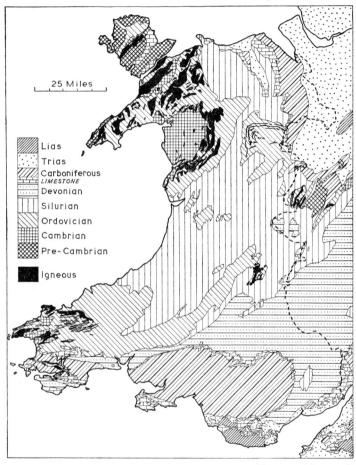

25 Miles

Lias
Trias
Carboniferous
LIMESTONE
Devonian
Silurian
Ordovician
Cambrian
Pre-Cambrian

Igneous

(Crown copyright reserved)

Fig. 17. Solid geology
(SOURCE: Ordnance Survey 1/625,000 series.)

Caldicot Level less than 5 per cent of the cropland was devoted to barley, and there was an appreciable decrease in the importance of the crop northwards along the shore of Cardigan Bay, under the influence of increasing coastal marsh. In the Vale of Clwyd, on the other hand, where soil drainage is impeded in winter only, the shortness of barley's growing season enabled it to reach maturity between the drying-out period in spring and the onset of the following winter. In more upland areas heavy rainfall and acid

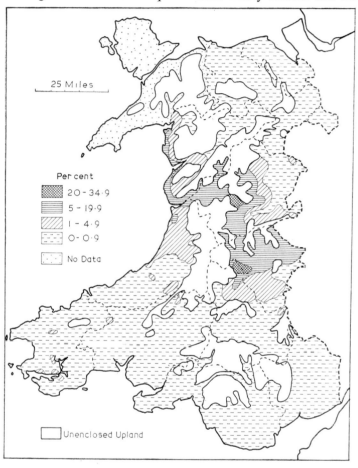

Fig. 18. Proportion of cropland in rye, 1801

(Source: P.R.O., H.O.67, 1, 6, 12–13, 21–2.)

soils reduced barley's share of the cropland to less than 20 per cent, but there was one notable exception, the limestone plateau of Flintshire (Fig. 17), where more than 35 per cent of the cropland was in barley.

An examination of Fig. 16 reveals clearly that the most important growing areas for barley were the coastlands of south-west Wales; the areas in which it has already been noted, the acreages of both wheat and oats were low. The growing season in these districts is the longest in Wales (Fig. 14) and it is surprising to find barley as the most important grain over such a wide area. It is tempting to see in this map the influence of the cooler summers of the west coast areas of Britain but this explanation is inconsistent both with the general distribution shown in Fig. 16 and also with what evidence there is for other areas at this time.[1] It is far more likely that the map reflects the influence of traditional farming methods in south-west Wales.

Rye (Fig. 18)

Rye is a particularly hardy plant which thrives under a great variety of conditions. It is less exacting in its soil requirements than any other important cereal provided the soil is properly drained. It tolerates considerable degrees of acidity and alkalinity and produces reasonable growth at low levels of fertility. In addition the plant requires a very short growing season and is well able to survive hard winters. When grown for grain under good conditions, however, it is usually less profitable than the other cereals and tends to be confined to land which is, in one way or another, unsuited to wheat, oats, or barley.

Before examining the distribution map it should be recalled that rye was included among the eight crops in the returns of 1801 as an afterthought. In the diocese of St. David's only, where special forms were printed, did rye appear as one of the listed crops. In the other dioceses the crop was entered on the form in manuscript by the diocesan clerk or the incumbent, or was omitted altogether. Although those returns which have no mention of rye are comparatively few in number,[2] the possibility that some acreages may be unrepresented in Fig. 18 cannot be ignored, especially in Glamorgan, where, of the eighty-seven forms returned, sixty-six have no entry for rye.

Fig. 18 shows that rye cropping was distributed over a limited area in central Wales where in no parish was it of great importance,

[1] E.g. H. C. K. Henderson, 'Agriculture in England and Wales in 1801', *Geographical Journal*, 118 (1952), 344.

[2] See D. Williams, op. cit., who distinguishes carefully in his transcription of the material between nil returns, and no entry against a crop.

judged by the percentage of cropland sometimes devoted to the other cereals. But in two small areas rye occupied more than 20 per cent of the cropland. The first was in the broken country of the Brecknockshire–Radnorshire border and the second, perched in the pass which provides one of the major routeways from Montgomeryshire to the west (Fig. 4). Over much of the highlands of north Radnorshire and west Montgomeryshire, and also upon the narrow coastal plain of Merioneth where poor soils are characteristic, more than 5 per cent of the cropland was in rye, but elsewhere in Wales the crop was unimportant.

The fact that rye was nowhere of great importance, and its association with areas physically poorly endowed, make it clear that rye was grown only where economic yields of wheat, oats, and barley were not expected. The unexacting nature of the plant allowed it to flourish where the land was most rugged, the soils poorest, and the growing season shortest.

Potatoes (Fig. 19)

The potato, like rye, tolerates a wide range of soil conditions but flourishes best where moisture is abundant and soil drainage good. The plant withstands considerable soil acidity but it does not thrive in calcareous soils. High temperatures during the time when the plant is developing its tubers reduces yield and so a cool growing season with at least moderate rainfall is an important climatic requirement. The special needs of early potatoes are, of course, irrelevant at this period. Potatoes were grown not only as farm field crops, but also in gardens, on pieces of waste ground, and sometimes around the borders of fields containing other crops. It is possible that many of the smaller potato patches were not included in the acreages returned.

Fig. 19 suggests that the comparison between potatoes and rye can be carried further. Like rye, the areas in which potatoes were most important tend, with a few small exceptions, to fringe the moorland core of the country, but the crop was not confined to central Wales, neither was there such a range in the amount of cropland which it occupied. From Mynydd Hiraethog in the north, to Mynydd Presely and the Black Mountains in the south (Fig. 4) between 5 per cent and 20 per cent of the cropland in upland areas was devoted to potatoes. Generally in lowland areas most parishes had 1–5 per cent of their cropland in potatoes, though in a number of limited areas the proportion is higher. More than 20 per cent of the cropland was occupied by the crop upon the river alluvium in the lower valleys of the Llwchwr and Cleddy Wen, and more than

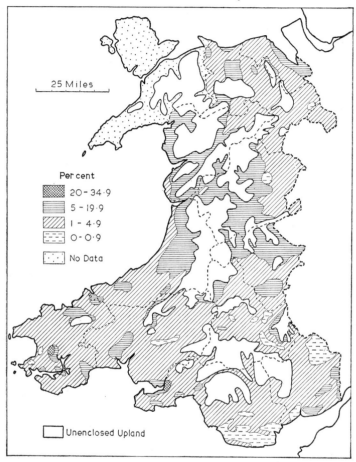

Fig. 19. Proportion of cropland in potatoes, 1801
(SOURCE: P.R.O., H.O.67, 1, 6, 12–13, 21–2.)

5 per cent around the mouths of the Teifi and Dee (Fig. 2). Geologically recent coastal plains, such as those of northern Merioneth and northern Denbighshire, also carried more than 5 per cent of cropland in potatoes. In two areas only, north-east Monmouthshire and the Vale of Glamorgan, were there many parishes with

less than 1 per cent of their cropland in potatoes; the two areas in which proportions of wheat, a crop with very different physical requirements, exceeded 50 per cent (Fig. 12).

The distribution map for potatoes, although quantitatively different from that for rye, illustrates the extent to which the crops performed similar functions. In the Vale of Glamorgan, where conditions are ideal for wheat and barley, many parishes grew no potatoes, but on the moorland fringes and in lowland areas of heavy wet soils sometimes as much as one-quarter of the cropland was devoted to the crop.

Peas (Fig. 20)

Peas are a hardy crop able to withstand relatively low temperatures, even during the seedling stage. But, as the crop approaches maturity, bright, dry weather is most desirable, and a wet harvest can prove disastrous. Peas are best adapted to well-drained medium loam soils, especially those which are calcareous, but sandy or gravelly land is also suitable.

Fig. 20 illustrates the importance of these physical requirements in determining the distribution of the crop. With one exception all the major growing areas occur where rainfall is under 40 inches a year (Fig. 13): in the eastern facing basins and on the north and south coasts. In most areas along the border 5–20 per cent of the cropland was in peas and one parish in Monmouthshire returned 28 per cent. But in the northern part of the borderland the heavy soils of the Cheshire Plain and Dee estuary restricted the crop and there was, in fact, a contrast between coastal Flintshire, where less than 5 per cent of the cropland was in peas, and the inland limestone plateau (Fig. 17), where there was over 5 per cent. In the Vale of Clwyd and in coastal Denbighshire peas again occupied more than 5 per cent of the cropland. In one small area only of the Vale of Glamorgan, upon soils developed from the Lias (Fig. 17), was the percentage of parish cropland in peas comparable with that in the borderland. Here in one parish peas occupied 22 per cent of the cropland.

Cardiganshire provides the major exception. Large areas of the county received more than 40 inches of rain annually and yet in only four parishes was less than 1 per cent of the cropland in peas; a marked contrast with the neighbouring county of Carmarthenshire.

But the contrast was merely one of degree. The same differences existed between the drier lowlands and the wetter uplands of Cardiganshire as in other parts of Wales. On the coast, four

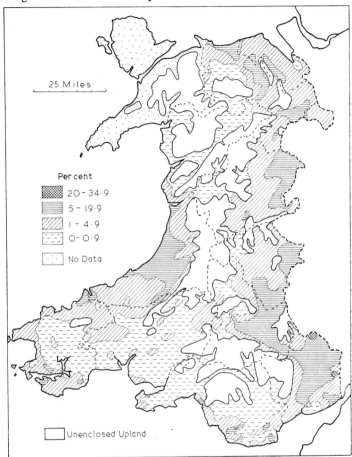

Fig. 20. Proportion of cropland in peas, 1801
(SOURCE: P.R.O., H.O.67, 1, 6, 12–13, 21–2.)

adjoining parishes had more than 10 per cent of their cropland devoted to peas while inland the influence of the higher ground (Fig. 4) is evident in the crop map.

The similarity between the ecological requirements of peas and barley is emphasized by a comparison of the two distribution maps

(Figs. 16, 20). In both maps there is a decrease in the importance of the crop with altitude, and in both, Flintshire is exceptional. In both maps the crop is restricted in areas of high water table, such as the Caldicot Level and the Cheshire Plain, and in both, values increase upon soils derived from calcareous parent materials. Quantitatively barley was the more important, but in all essentials the maps are akin.

Beans (Fig. 21).

Unlike peas, beans are sensitive to extremes of temperature and require relatively large amounts of moisture throughout the growing season.[1] They are best suited to heavy soils, but will grow in most other types provided that there is sufficient moisture at the right time. Beans require a very long growing period and ripen late in the season.

In 1801 few beans were grown in Wales (Fig. 21). Of the eleven counties for which data is available one returned more than 100 acres, namely Flintshire, four counties, Brecknockshire, Merioneth, Montgomeryshire, and Pembrokeshire, returned less than 25 acres, and Radnorshire none. While allowance has to be made for understatement and for the missing parishes, the actual total must have been very small. What beans were grown were highly localized. In each of the counties of Brecknock, Carmarthen, Flint, and Pembroke, over half the acreage was returned by one parish. In Glamorgan and Monmouthshire, the only two counties in which the proportion of cropland under beans in any parish exceeded 5 per cent, the map illustrates the same compactness of the distribution. But with such small quantities grown it is hazardous to speculate too much about causation. Certainly all the areas which had more than 1 per cent of the cropland in beans are at or below 600 feet (Fig. 4), though some receive annual rainfall of less than 30 inches and others of nearly 50 inches (Fig. 13). The moisture retaining qualities of the alluvial soil in the lower Vale of Clwyd and the Caldicot Level may account for the growth of beans in those areas, but elsewhere the detailed locating factors are not clear.

Turnips and rape (Fig. 22)

It is unfortunate that turnips and rape were returned together as this hinders the interpretation of Fig. 22. Both are crops which

[1] R. H. Hooker, op. cit.

require a moist summer and both thrive best on light soils as a fine tilth is needed, especially at the germination stage; but turnips are of special significance at this period. Though turnips had been

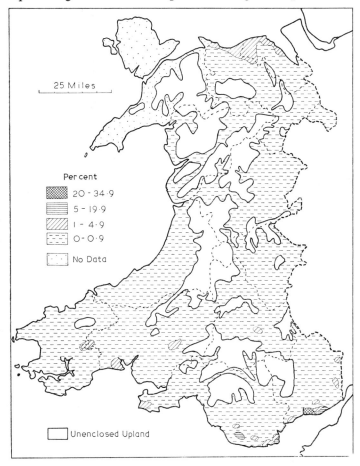

Fig. 21. Proportion of cropland in beans, 1801
(SOURCE: P.R.O., H.O.67, 1, 6, 12–13, 21–2.)

grown for some time as a garden crop in Wales, it was not until the turn of the eighteenth century that the adoption of turnip husbandry introduced them extensively as a field crop. Fortunately many of the incumbents making the returns either deleted the word 'rape' from their forms, or gave the acreage of turnips separately. These returns suggest that the distribution shown represents broadly that of turnips alone, and so the map gives a clear indication of the extent to which new farming methods had penetrated into Wales by 1801.

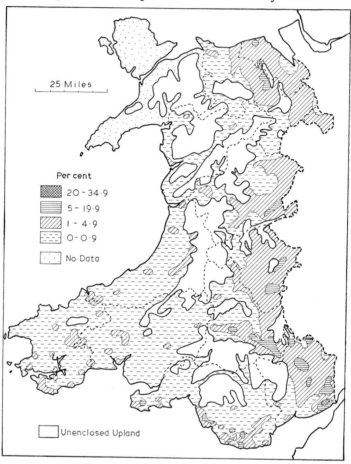

25 Miles

Per cent

20 - 34·9

5 - 19·9

1 - 4·9

0 - 0·9

No Data

Unenclosed Upland

Fig. 22. Proportion of cropland in turnips and rape, 1801
(SOURCE: P.R.O., H.O.67, 1, 6, 12–13, 21–2.)

The distribution of turnips, like that of barley and peas, was distinctly lowland in character (Figs. 16, 20, 22), but unlike those crops there were no areas where turnips were of importance to the west of the moorland heart of Wales. In a number of scattered parishes more than 1 per cent of the cropland was in turnips and, significantly, in Gower one parish returned 7 per cent of its crop acreage as turnips, but generally the crop was little grown. To the east of the heartland in many lowland areas, turnips occupied more than 5 per cent of the cropland. In the Vales of Clwyd, Severn, Wye, and Usk the crop was well established, and in one Monmouthshire parish 27 per cent of the cropland was in turnips. In areas of heavy soil, such as the Caldicot Level, the crop was excluded completely.

Fig. 22 is the resultant of two forces. The first was the spread from the east of fresh agricultural ideas; a spread in which the initiative was wholly with the landowners and their tenants, but which was also much influenced by physical access to the source of the new techniques in eastern England (Figs. 3, 4). In the light of this diffusion the decrease in the importance of turnips westwards and also the disjointed distribution pattern, especially to the west of the moorland core, becomes understandable. In the border shires, the crop may well have been fully adjusted to its physical, economic, and cultural environment, but in the counties of Cardigan, Carmarthen, Merioneth, and Pembroke there existed what, in another context, might have been termed a 'pioneer fringe'. The second force which the map reflects was the much more local influence of soil texture and drainage. Even in the more easterly parts of the country turnip husbandry, with its emphasis upon constant tillage and crops requiring well-drained soils, was limited very closely to areas of low rainfall and light land; areas to which it was ecologically and technologically best adapted.

So far in this study of cropping in 1801 the argument had been confined to an examination of the distribution of the individual crops. This approach by no means exhausts the possibilities of interpretation, but it has given a very clear idea of the influence which physical factors exerted upon the utilisation of cropland at this period. It is generally accepted that it was the coming of the railways in the mid-nineteenth century, followed by the development of road transport, which established the crop specialization that exists today.[1] But before this, in 1801, the evidence presented suggests that more local specialization had grown up related to the ecological characteristics of the various crops; a feature specially noticeable in Wales where physical conditions are so diverse. It is difficult to judge to what extent this specialization implies exchange

[1] L.D. Stamp, op. cit., 62–3.

of commodities. Undoubtedly much of the produce was consumed locally. For example, in south Cardiganshire and Gower, where the proportion of cropland in barley approached 50 per cent, that grain was used for breadmaking,[2] and in Merioneth, where often 75 per cent of the cropland was in oats, oatmeal provided the bulk of the diet.[3] But there is also abundant evidence of trade in farm produce,[4] though not on the scale of more recent times. The returns of 1801 seem to mark a mid-way stage in the growth of specialized agricultural regions in this country, between the self-sufficient systems derived directly from Welsh tribalism and Anglo–Norman feudalism, and the extensive crop specialization of the post-railway period. At the same time, as the distribution map of turnips and rape (Fig. 20) so amply demonstrated, the forces of agricultural change were vigorously overcoming traditional localized techniques and tastes. It was a stage at which many areas were no longer agriculturally self-sufficient, at which extensive regional specialization in cropping had not yet appeared, but at which the growing knowledge of sound agricultural practices was pressing crop specialization upon physically favourable areas to the limit imposed by the effective demand for the commodities.

[2] P.R.O., H.O.67, 22 (Ciliau Aeron, Port Einon).
[3] P.R.O., H.O.42, 54 (Llanfawr).
[4] Supra 48; see also G. E. Fussell and C. Goodman, 'Traffic in farm produce in eighteenth-century England', *Agricultural History*, 12 (1938), 355–68. Evidence of trade in market garden produce also exists, especially from the area around Cardiff. See W. E. Minchinton, 'Bristol—metropolis of the west in the eighteenth century', *Transactions of the Royal Historical Society*, 5th series, 4 (1954), 74.

CHAPTER 5

THE ACREAGE RETURNS OF 1801:
CROP COMPETITION

THE study of the distributions of the individual crops in 1801 is a necessary stage in their analysis, but it is, from a geographical point of view, incomplete because it isolates each crop from its context. All crops which have broadly similar ecological requirements are directly, or potentially, competitors for growing space, and most crops are grown as elements of rotational systems. Attention must be directed at the acreage-strength of crops in relation to that of rivals to remedy this deficiency.

Methods of approach

The simplest means of examining the competitive strengths of crops is by an analysis of crop-acreage rank order; that is, by listing the crops in each parish in order of decreasing acreage, and then studying together those which attain the same places on the list. In Figs. 24–7 the first, second, third, and fourth most important crops in 1801 have been represented by non-quantitative geometric symbols. As before these have been located over the major settlements of the parishes, and those parishes for which no material exists have been omitted. Some of the more subtle differences revealed by the crop distribution maps are lost by this method. For example, first ranking crops may vary in importance in their parishes between 90 per cent of the cropland, the figure for oats in Llanycil, Merioneth, and 29 per cent of the cropland, the figure for wheat in Newchurch, Monmouthshire. Even so a clearer picture of the relative importance of the various crops in different areas is obtained.

The second method employed is designed to identify those combinations of crops for every parish which may be considered typical or dominant, and it thus supplies many of the deficiencies of both the single crop and rank order analyses. Each crop combination is derived by objective means from the Acreage Returns and a standard notation adopted to simplify description.[1] For example,

---

[1] W—wheat, O—oats, B—barley, R—rye, Pt—potatoes, Pe—peas, Be—beans, T—turnips and rape.

a parish in which wheat and barley were the dominant crops is classified as WB, and a parish with a wheat-oats-barley-peas combination is given an index of WOBPe. The crop combination index will clearly provide grounds for speculation about contemporary rotational practices. A parish in which the Norfolk four-course system (wheat, turnips, barley, clover) was well established would probably have a WBT index, or at least include turnips in its crop combination, but in a parish not influenced by the new ideas these characteristics would be absent.

Crop combination indices have been calculated by using a modification of the method devised by Weaver.[1] In each parish the percentages of cropland devoted to all eight crops can be ranked in descending order and these form a distinctive 'curve' which represents the relative standing of all crops in that parish. The crops which typify the parish lie at the upper end of the curve; the problem is to decide how many shall be included in the index. This can be done by making comparisons between the parish crop curve and a set of ideal curves which represent theoretical situations.[2] If monoculture were practised, then 100 per cent of the cropland would be in one crop and 0 per cent in all others; if a two-crop parish, 50 per cent of the cropland would be in each of two crops and 0 per cent in all others; if a three-crop parish, 33·3 per cent of the cropland would be in each of three crops and 0 per cent in all others; and so on to an eight-crop parish in which 12·5 per cent of the cropland would be in each of eight crops. The deviations of the parish crop curve from each theoretical curve can be expressed as the sum of the squares of the differences between the percentage of cropland devoted to each crop and the corresponding point on the theoretical curve (Σd^2). The theoretical curve to which the parish crop curve most approximates, judged by the least value of Σd^2, then serves to identify the number of representative crops. There is no need when applying this method to the Acreage Returns for Wales to distinguish, as Weaver does, the major field crops from other crops or to omit from the calculation those crops which occupy less than 1 per cent of the cropland. Neither is it necessary to employ the special category,

[1] J. C. Weaver, 'Crop combination regions in the Middle West', *Geographical Review*, 44 (1954), 175–200. The method is also slightly different from that described in D. Thomas, 'The statistical and cartographic treatment of the Acreage Returns of 1801', *Geographical Studies*, 5 (1958), 15–25.

[2] The arguments favouring this approach are outlined in D. Thomas, op. cit., 19–20.

'dominant crop', used in an earlier study.[1] Having established the typical crops, no attention is paid to crop rank as this aspect is fully covered by the rank order analysis. For example, BWO, BOW, OWB and all other variants of rank are classified as WOB, the nomenclature order following that shown above in the presentation of the standard notation.

An example will illustrate the method. For the parish of Llan-gors, Brecknockshire, the percentage of the cropland under the various crops may be summarised as follows: W 32, O 31·5, B 17·1, Pe 11·7, Pt 4·4, T 3·3, R nil, Be nil. These values give the parish crop curve which must be matched with the theoretical curves to determine the number of representative crops. Rye and beans were not grown and so the calculation need be carried no further than the sixth crop. Fig. 23 illustrates visually the matching process. Σd^2 is least where

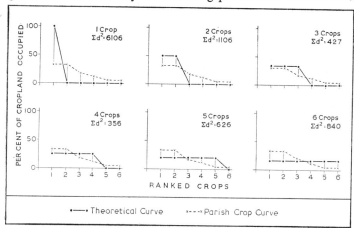

Fig. 23. Determination of the crop combination index for Llan-gors, Brecknockshire
(SOURCE: P.R.O., H.O.67, 22.)

the parish crop curve is compared with the theoretical curve representing a four-crop parish; that is, Llan-gors is more like a four-crop parish than any other, and so the crop combination index is WOBPe.

With over 500 returns available, it is not surprising that in an area as physically, and at this period culturally, diverse as Wales the technique should produce more than twenty different crop combinations. Of these, there are eight which occur repeatedly; the others appear much less frequently and are much more scattered in location. In Fig. 28 the distribution of the eight major indices is

[1] Ibid., 22.

7

shown by distinctive geometric symbols while the remaining indices are undifferentiated. The method of mapping follows that used for crop rank order.

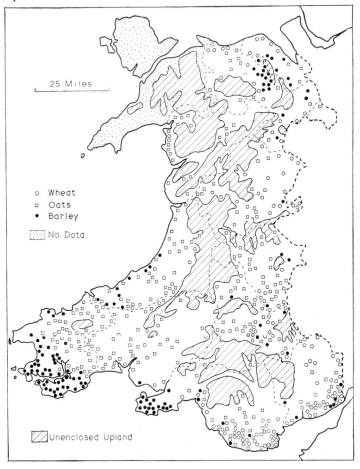

Fig. 24. First ranking crops, 1801
(Source: P.R.O., H.O.67, 1, 6, 12–13, 21–2.)

Crop rank order

The map showing the most important crop in each parish (Fig. 24) is, as might be expected, dominated by the three major grains, wheat, oats, and barley. But over its area there are marked contrasts.

Oats, the crop which appears most frequently in first place, were clearly dominant in upland areas; only on the limestone plateau of Flintshire was the crop replaced by barley. In the eastern counties of Wales oats as first crop generally gave way to wheat with decreasing altitude. Oats were in first place on Mynydd Hiraethog (Fig. 4) but wheat dominated the narrow coastal plain, and the same contrast existed between upland Glamorgan and the Vale. Along the border wheat was first crop in the larger lowland areas, such as eastern Monmouthshire, and also where the main streams, the Severn, Wye, and Usk (Fig. 2), extended lowland conditions westward. Occasionally in these eastern lowlands barley attained first rank, but in the Vale of Clwyd almost every parish returned barley as the first crop.

In the western half of the country the picture was very different. Oats were everywhere in first place in upland areas but they were also leading crop over much of the lowlands. To the east oats had been of importance in the lowlands only in a limited area fringing the Cheshire Plain and upon the littoral of Recent age between Cardiff and Newport, but to the west in the Vale of Ffestiniog, on the coastlands of Merioneth and north Cardiganshire, and over much of lowland Carmarthenshire and Pembrokeshire oats ranked first. Where oats were replaced by another crop in south-west Cardiganshire, south-west Pembrokeshire and Gower that crop was not wheat but barley, which seems to have gained its position mainly at the expense of oats since the time of the Anglo-Norman colonization.[1] Not one parish in the counties of Cardigan, Carmarthen, Merioneth and Pembroke returned wheat as first crop.

When studying the distributions of the individual crops it was noted that there were, with a number, differences in the intensity of cropping between east and west. This was a most noticeable feature of the map showing the distribution of turnips and rape, but it was also true of other crops. Fig. 24 crystallizes these differences for the three major grains and suggests the importance in the eastern part of the country not only of the physical characteristics of lowland areas but also of access to ideas from the east, where wheaten bread

[1] Cf. Fig. 24 with W. Rees, *South Wales and the March, 1284–1415* (Oxford, 1924), 187–8; F. V. Emery, 'West Glamorgan farming, *circa* 1580–1620', *National Library of Wales Journal*, 9 (1956), 397; B. E. Howells, 'Pembrokeshire farming, *circa* 1580–1620', *National Library of Wales Journal*, 9 (1956), 246.

was far more common. To the west of the upland core physical inaccessibility was clearly an important determinant. The point is emphasized by the occurrence of wheat as first rank crop further to the west along the northern and southern coast routes (Fig. 3) than anywhere else in the country, though the length of the growing season on these coasts may have been contributory (Fig. 14). The evidence in the north is incomplete but in south Wales despite the facility of the traditional through route, wheat was first crop no further west than Swansea. The contrast between south Pembrokeshire and Gower, where barley was first crop, and the Vale of Glamorgan, where, despite the widespread occurrence of calcareous soils, wheat was the most important crop in almost every parish, is marked; a difference which, it has already been stressed, cannot wholly be attributed to the ecological requirements of barley and wheat.

The prevalence of long-established tastes and practices in west Wales is illustrated by the map showing crops ranking second in each parish (Fig. 25). In Cardiganshire every parish returned oats and barley in the first two places and, with one exception, in every parish in Carmarthenshire barley held second place after oats. In north Pembrokeshire and in coastal Merioneth the same crops occupied the first two places. In all these areas oats and barley must have been important elements in the diet, not only as bread constituents but also for various types of porridge though, of course, barley was also used for malting.[1] Oats and barley are crops which integrate well with a pastoral economy, a rôle for which wheat is unsuited. In south Pembrokeshire and Gower, on the other hand, where barley ranked first, wheat was more usually second crop. This clearly sets apart from the rest of west Wales the two southern peninsulas, where cropping practices may well reflect the markedly different cultural heritage.[2]

In the eastern part of the country wheat frequently held second place to oats in the highlands, in central Montgomeryshire, south Radnorshire, and northern Glamorgan, but this was not true of all

[1] A. W. Ashby and I. L. Evans, *The agriculture of Wales and Monmouthshire* (Cardiff, 1944), 20.

[2] See E. G. Bowen (ed.), *Wales, a physical, historical, and regional geography* (London, 1957), 340–3, 425–7.

areas. On Mynydd Hiraethog and in north-west Brecknockshire barley was second, but in west Montgomeryshire and north-west Radnorshire oats were followed by rye. On the limestone plateau of

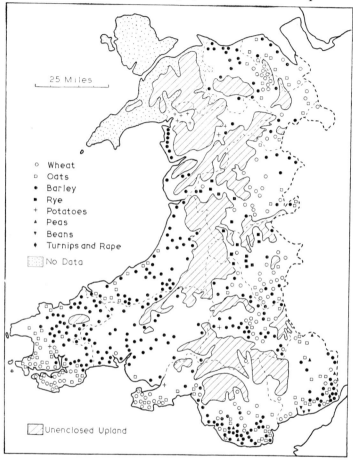

25 Miles

○ Wheat
□ Oats
● Barley
■ Rye
+ Potatoes
▲ Peas
▼ Beans
◆ Turnips and Rape
No Data

Unenclosed Upland

Fig. 25. Second ranking crops, 1801
(Source: P.R.O., H.O.67, 1, 6, 12–13, 21–2.)

Flintshire, where barley was first crop, oats were in second place. In the eastern lowlands barley was most often second crop; on the north Wales coast, in north-east Montgomeryshire, in the valleys of the Wye and Usk, in south-east Monmouthshire, and in the Vale of Glamorgan the crop occurred more frequently in second place than any other. Where barley was first crop wheat almost always ranked second. There are examples in most areas but the most notable is the Vale of Clwyd.

Unlike the map showing first ranking crops the full range of crops returned in 1801 appears in Fig. 25. The widespread occurrence of rye in second rank in central Wales has already been mentioned but three non-grain crops should also be noted. Potatoes attained second place in a few scattered parishes but in north-west Merioneth there was a compact area where the crop ranked second behind oats. In three adjacent parishes on the Caldicot Level beans were second in importance to wheat, signifying the physical character of that coastal area. In Monmouthshire, turnips and rape ranked second in one parish to barley.

A comparison of the maps showing crops of first and second rank is instructive from another point of view (cf. Figs. 24 and 25). It is clear that in most parts of the country barley was either in first or in second place; north-west Merioneth provides the only exception in the west, and the uplands of central and south Wales the important exception in the east. It is thus possible to support the contention of Ashby and Evans,[1] based upon later evidence, that barley has always been more important in Wales than its nearest competitor, wheat.

In the map showing crops ranking third in each parish (Fig. 26) the areal pattern is much fragmented, but the map is valuable because it emphasizes the distinctiveness of certain regions where the first three crops consistently attained the same rank. The most obvious of these is Carmarthenshire and north Pembrokeshire, where wheat was third crop after oats and barley, a sequence which also occurred in north Cardiganshire. In south Pembrokeshire and Gower barley and wheat were followed by oats; it is significant that elsewhere in west Wales wheat did not appear among the first three crops. In north-west Merioneth barley was third crop after oats and potatoes but along the north Merioneth coast potatoes consistently held third place after oats and barley. This same sequence was also characteristic of many of the areas fringing the moorland in the western parts of the country. In central Cardiganshire the frequent occurrence of peas in third place is a feature of the map.

[1] A. W. Ashby and I. L. Evans, op. cit., 19–20.

In the eastern part of Wales barley was fairly commonly third crop in upland areas, but on the Flintshire plateau wheat was third. In the lowlands, oats occurred frequently in third place in all areas

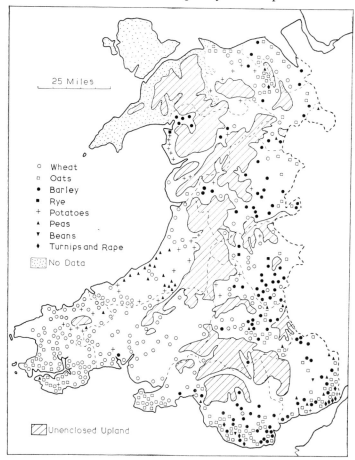

25 Miles

○ Wheat
□ Oats
● Barley
■ Rye
+ Potatoes
▲ Peas
▼ Beans
◆ Turnips and Rape

No Data

Unenclosed Upland

Fig. 26. Third ranking crops, 1801
(Source: P.R.O., H.O.67, 1, 6, 12–13, 21–2.)

except that in the extreme south-east of the Vale of Glamorgan, where barley was third crop. Two non-grain crops diversify this pattern. Parishes in which peas ranked third were well scattered throughout the eastern lowlands with no concentration in any particular area; the growth of turnips and rape, on the other hand,

gave distinctiveness to south-east Monmouthshire. In addition to
the one parish in which turnips and rape ranked second, five other
parishes returned the crops in third place. Further to the west in

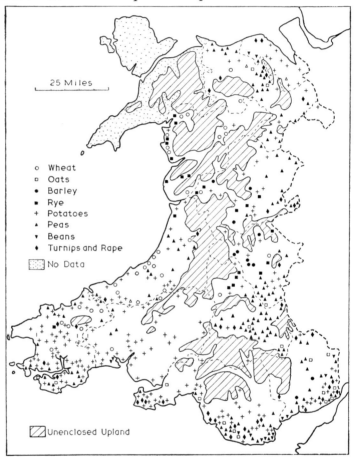

Fig. 27. Fourth ranking crops, 1801
(SOURCE: P.R.O., H.O.67, 1, 6, 12–13, 21–2.)

the Vale of Glamorgan turnips and rape ranked third in three
parishes and also in one parish in the Vale of Clwyd. In each instance
the crops in first and second places were wheat and barley; an
association which strongly suggests the widespread adoption of
turnip husbandry in these parishes and which supports an argument

already advanced that the distribution of turnips at this period gives a clear guide to the progress of agricultural reform.

The map showing fourth ranking crops (Fig. 27) is dominated by potatoes and peas. With the exception of central Brecknockshire, south Radnorshire and the Vale of Clwyd there was no extensive area in which potatoes were unrepresented either in fourth place or higher. The ubiquity of the crop suggests that it was grown for local human or animal consumption but its position, generally in fourth place, indicates that it played a far less important rôle in the economy than the grain crops which achieved higher rankings. Peas ranked fourth in areas accessible to the east; predominantly in the valleys of the Wye and Usk, but also along the north Wales coast, in the Vale of Clwyd, in eastern Montgomeryshire, and in the Vale of Glamorgan.

A number of other crops which occurred in fourth place deserve mention. Wheat was fairly frequently fourth crop in west Wales and in some parishes, for example six in north-west Merioneth, the crop was not among the first four. This emphasizes how unimportant wheat was in the west in 1801 in comparison with the east of the country, where the crop was in either first or second place in most areas. Turnips and rape appear quite often as fourth crop, and again the distribution confirms the pattern noted earlier. In south-east Monmouthshire the area in which turnips and rape ranked second or third is ringed by parishes in which the crops were returned in fourth place. In Fig. 27 turnips and rape appear frequently in the Vale of Glamorgan, but westwards in Gower and south Pembrokeshire the crop symbol is less apparent. Over the rest of the map the crops occur in association with the major routeways from the east, along the north coast, the Vale of Clwyd, and the valleys of the Severn, Wye, and Usk (cf. Fig. 3), and in a number of scattered places in the west. Beans were fourth crop in a small area to the south-west and to the east of Cardiff. It was in a physically similar area to the south-east of Newport that beans attained second rank (Fig. 25).

The analysis of crop-acreage rank order is, in many ways, a limited method but it is one from which an important point has emerged. Not only has it illustrated once more the influence of physical factors but it has also shown the very real differences which existed between

east and west Wales during the Napoleonic wars. The effects of the
accessibility of the east to the practices and tastes of England clearly
emerge in the crop rank maps, while in the west an older order

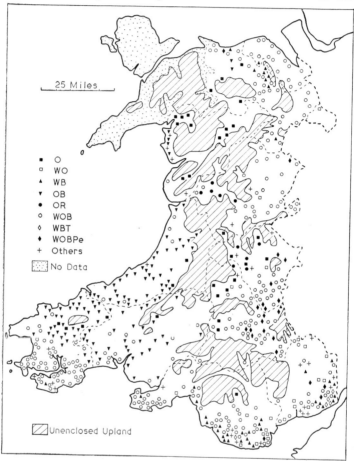

Fig. 28. Crop combination indices, 1801
(SOURCE: P.R.O., H.O.67, 1, 6, 12–13, 21–2.)

prevailed. Here vestiges of a previous diffusion of agricultural
methods seem to have persisted in Gower and south Pembrokeshire;
locations that strongly suggest a certain degree of continuity from
the period of Anglo-Norman colonization, which probably facilitated
the gradual spread, at some time before 1801, of a lowland crop,

barley. Each map is an incomplete palimpsest; always the more rewarding kind.

Crop combinations

The parishes to which the eight major crop combination indices have been allocated tended to be distributed in fairly well-defined regions (Fig. 28), and none of the regions was more consistently located than that composed of parishes designated O (oats mono-culture). As might be expected these fringed the upland moors, but it is noticeable that they were more frequent on the western and northern edges of the main moorland mass than to the east and south, where few parishes returned sufficiently large proportions of their cropland in oats to achieve monoculture status, despite the large areas shown in Fig. 15 with more than 50 per cent of cropland under the crop. A very small number only of the parishes in which oats ranked first crop (Fig. 24) are shown as O parishes in Fig. 28, and these clearly represent the highland core of the area in which the hardier grains were grown; an area analogous to what has been recognized as the Welsh heartland.[1]

Closely associated with the O parishes were those in which oats and rye typify the crops grown. OR parishes fringed the unenclosed uplands in north-west Radnorshire and in western Montgomery-shire; areas which, if they do not possess all the characteristics of the heartland, certainly experience extreme physical conditions. It is not surprising, therefore, to find in these areas combinations containing rye; a crop less exacting in its requirements than any other returned in 1801.

Surrounding these regions were parishes which are typified by combinations of crops characteristic of neither completely upland nor lowland areas; that is, their crop combination indices contain both crops like oats, usually to be found in the uplands, and domi-nantly lowland crops like wheat or peas. Easily the most numerous of this kind were the WOB parishes. In Denbighshire they occupied all but the Vale of Clwyd and the higher parts of Mynydd Hiraethog, and in Flintshire every parish was designated WOB except one in the detached portion of the county. Similarly in eastern Montgomery-shire, south Radnorshire, central Brecknockshire, central Monmouth-shire, and the uplands of Glamorgan WOB parishes dominated.

[1] E. G. Bowen (ed.), op. cit., 271.

The importance of the crop combination in the border shires is such that in an earlier study of the Welsh borderland[1] the WOB region was recognized as one particularly characteristic of transitional conditions between upland and lowland, and constituted a Borderland Zone in the crop landscape. In west Wales WOB parishes were dominant only in south Pembrokeshire and Gower again emphasizing the distinctiveness of those areas, but a few WOB parishes also occurred in north Cardiganshire, west Montgomeryshire and in scattered places in lowland Carmarthenshire.

Numerically the next most important of the peripheral crop combinations is OB. Parishes in which oats and barley were the major crops were widely distributed in Cardiganshire, Carmarthenshire, north Pembrokeshire, and on the north-west coast of Merioneth. There were two parishes on the fringe of Mynydd Hiraethog in west Denbighshire, but it is notable that the combination did not occur in any of the other eastern counties where, apart from the highland regions, wheat appeared in every combination.

Two further crop combinations contain crops which are ecologically dissimilar WOBPe parishes were associated principally with areas of lowland accessible to the east, and occurred mainly in the valleys of the Lugg, Wye, and Usk. There was a close link between these parishes and the WOB parishes; a relationship which is made clearer by a study of both the Welsh and the English border counties.[2] WO parishes occurred in three small groups in south Wales; one around Cardiff, another around Newport and a third in east Monmouthshire. The single parish in the detached part of Flintshire formed part of an extensive WO region covering most of the Cheshire Plain. In almost all these parishes oats appeared not because climatic conditions were severe, as in the uplands, but because each parish contained large areas of heavy soil.

Lastly there are two crop combinations, WB and WBT, which are composed of crops typical of lowland areas. The WB parishes were by far the more numerous, and occurred in three main areas. They were frequent in south-east Monmouthshire, where the parishes shown in Fig. 26 form part only of a more extensive region covering

[1] D. Thomas, 'Agricultural changes in the Welsh Borderland: a cultural diffusion at the turn of the eighteenth century', *Transactions of the Honourable Society of Cymmrodorion* (1961), 101–14.

[2] Idem., 'The Acreage Returns of 1801 for the Welsh Borderland', *Transactions and Papers, 1959*, Institute of British Geographers, 26 (1959), 181.

much of the Forest of Dean.[1] To the west the combination was strongly represented in the Vale of Glamorgan, but in one parish only in Gower and in one in south Pembrokeshire were wheat and barley dominant crops. In north Wales seven WB parishes were grouped in the Vale of Clwyd; an area which has been anomalous in many of the distributions discussed. There has been evidence, for example, in the maps showing the distributions of peas and turnips (Figs. 20, 22), of its links with lowland England, and this seems to be confirmed here. Despite the fairly consistent third ranking of oats (Fig. 24) the crop was clearly not as important as it was in Gower or south Pembrokeshire, where a similar rank order existed but with a WOB crop combination. The Vale of Clwyd thus emerges at this period, in both a physical and an agricultural sense, as a lowland enclave within the highlands.

Though the number of WBT parishes was small, their importance cannot be overestimated. With the WB parishes, the absence of one of the poorer grains from the crop combination and the frequent third or fourth ranking of turnips (Figs. 26, 27) suggested that an ingressive element existed, but the WBT index provides more than mere suggestion. It is significant of the widespread adoption of the Norfolk system. The four WBT parishes in south-east Monmouthshire and the single parish in the Vale of Glamorgan summarize the progress of the diffusion of turnip husbandry into Wales in 1801.

From this discussion it is clear that cropping in Wales in 1801 is divisible into three broad regions, each with diverse components. These have been illustrated in Fig. 29, a generalized version of Fig. 28 in which the eight main crop combinations have been allocated among the three major groups. First, in the centre of the country and fringing much of the moorland edge were the Highland Regions, consisting of the parishes in which oats and rye were typical crops. Secondly, surrounding these regions and covering most of the remainder of Wales were the Peripheral Regions: WO, OB, WOB, and WOBPe.[2] Thirdly, along the south Wales coast as far west as Neath and in the Vale of Clwyd were the Ingressive Regions, WB, WBT, showing markedly the influence of lowland England.

Despite the understatement of acreages, the gaps in the coverage and the omission from the survey of grassland, undoubtedly the most

[1] Ibid., 181.
[2] 'Peripheral' is used in a strictly spatial sense. It does not imply that the regions are in any way subordinate.

important element in the Welsh agricultural scene, the inclusion
of which would have revealed the variations in the importance of
cropland from place to place, the Acreage Returns of 1801 have

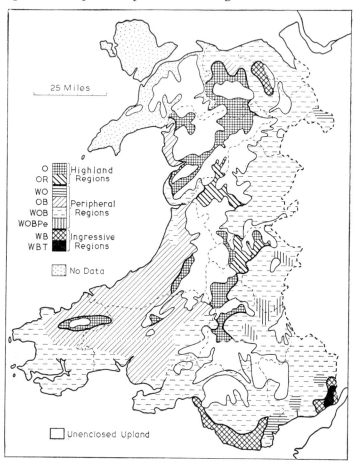

Fig. 29. Crop combination regions, 1801
(Source: P.R.O., H.O.67, 1, 6, 12–13, 21–2.)

yielded valuable information and as a source of material on cropping
during the Napoleonic wars have proved unique. No other source
gives data on a parish basis which can be used to illustrate the detailed
differences in cropping from region to region. No other source
provides a countrywide coverage in which the returns from different

areas are so standardized, comparable, and unambiguous. No other source refers to a single season or was compiled over so short a time; an important consideration in a period of change. The use of appropriate and complementary methods of analysis clearly can do much to overcome the inherent disadvantages of the material. Not least among the merits of the techniques used is that, out of the mass of data incorporated in the returns of 1801, one final summary map can be produced showing crop regions (Fig. 29). Because of the detail of the data from which this map was derived, and because of the nature of this study, it is desirable that these regions should provide a basis for the ordering of subsequent discussion.

CHAPTER 6

THE CENSUSES OF 1801 AND 1811

Problems of interpretation

UNLIKE the Acreage Returns of 1801 the earliest Censuses of Great Britain, the first and second of which were taken in 1801 and 1811, were supported by the authority of acts of parliament.[1] The official enumerators, generally the overseers of the poor, who made the house-to-house enquiries, and the local Justices of the Peace, before whom the Census forms were attested,[2] were also far less dependent upon oral information; they were well-placed to judge the veracity of the answers given, and, in any case, numbers of people and houses were far easier quantities to assess than acreages devoted to crops. Evasion of the kind so prevalent in the compilation of the Acreage Returns does not seem to have been possible, or desirable, but other omissions, misunderstandings, and sometimes the methods employed, have left the accuracy of the early Censuses open to question.

Probably the most valuable critique is that of John Rickman, who prepared the published abstracts of the first four enumerations (1801–31). In a note in the *Enumeration abstract* of the 1801 Census he considered the returns of the overseers of the poor.[3] The replies to the question on the number of families occupying the houses in each parish were said to be unreliable, partly because the question had been variously interpreted and partly because it had sometimes been left unanswered. The replies to the related question on uninhabited houses were also ambiguous. In some parishes houses returned as uninhabited were mostly ruined or deserted, in others they were composed mainly of houses being built, and consequently not yet habitable. But the question on occupations seems to have caused greatest uncertainty. Returns under three heads were required:

    I   persons chiefly employed in agriculture;
    II persons chiefly employed in trade, manufacture, or handicraft;
    III all other persons not comprised in the two preceding classes.

---

[1] *Guides to official sources, No. 2, Census reports of Great Britain 1801–1931* (H.M.S.O., London, 1951), 2.

[2] Ibid., 105.

[3] *Census 1801*, 496.

Rickman attributed the inconsistent replies to the fact that persons not belonging exclusively to any of the three categories were sometimes returned in more than one, so that the total of the occupation columns failed to coincide with total population. An examination of the material for Wales shows that there were more serious defects than those resulting from double counting, which rarely seems to have taken place. Logically, only active workers in farming, trade, manufacturing, and handicraft should have been included in the first two categories; those engaged in all other occupations, such as domestic servants or officers of the Church or State, together with the women who remained at home, children, old-aged and unemployed, should have been classified under the third heading. In quite a number of parishes the question was obviously interpreted in this way. The figures for Llanblethian, Glamorgan, for example (I 73, II 28, III 374, population total 475), show roughly the balance that might be expected. But in a large number of other parishes the question was interpreted differently. In such parishes as Llanfihangel Torymynydd, Monmouthshire (I 70, II 8, III Nil, population total 78), and Burton, Pembrokeshire (I 457, II Nil, III Nil, population total 457), it is clear that not only actual workers, but also their entire families and dependants were included in the occupation totals.

In another publication Rickman doubted the accuracy of the replies to the remaining question put to the overseers of the poor; that which asked for the return of parish population totals.[1] The figures, he thought, were rather low because some returns were wanting and in others there were omissions, but he could not estimate the amount of the deficiency. Later, when comparing the results of the 1811 Census with that of 1801 he modified this view.[2] More than two-thirds of the population increase between 1801 and 1811 could be verified by an analysis of registered baptisms and burials, which suggested that the whole increase was real, and not a result of omissions at the earlier date.

In the Census of 1811 Rickman made an attempt to prevent many of the inaccuracies of the first enumeration. The question about uninhabited houses was divided so that separate totals were given

[1] J. R[ickman], *Observations on the results of the Population Act, 41 Geo. III* (London, 1802), 9.
[2] *Census 1811,* xxvi.

8

of houses building and those uninhabited for any other reason. A comparison of the two figures was intended to provide an index to the prosperity of each parish. The question on occupations was so phrased that, instead of the number of persons chiefly employed in the various categories as in 1801, the number of families was required. As might be expected, the question again caused misunderstandings. Some parishes still returned the number of persons employed and others figures based upon households rather than families, but on this occasion all inconsistencies were settled by correspondence with the enumerators.[1]

The unreliability of the early Censuses seems to have been partly responsible for the lack of detailed systematic work making use of the source. Gonner preferred the 1841 estimates of the pre-Census population of England to the series of figures which resulted from the 1801 enquiry[2] and more recently Wilkinson, in his study of Census returns of occupations and industries, dismissed the 1801 figures as inconsistent and therefore practically useless.[3] The more ambitious scale of the Censuses from 1841 onwards has also encouraged work on periods after that date. The number of population studies of the period 1841–61[4] is in marked contrast with the volume of work on the earlier Censuses, despite the severe contemporary criticisms of the 1861 returns.[5] But, as with the 1801 Acreage Returns, appropriate statistical and cartographic treatment can do much to overcome the defects in the early Censuses, though, of course, however careful the methods, the inaccuracies of enumeration cannot be removed completely.

Treatment of the data

There is no sure means of checking the parish population totals of the 1801 and 1811 Censuses and so it is impossible to judge Rickman's conclusions about their accuracy or to make any corrections. Fortunately no strong reason exists for supposing that the

[1] Ibid., x.
[2] E. C. K. Gonner, 'The population of England in the eighteenth century', *Journal of the Royal Statistical Society*, 86 (1913), 261–303.
[3] H. R. Wilkinson, 'The mapping of Census returns of occupations and industries', *Geography*, 37 (1952), 38.
[4] E.g. H. C. Darby, 'The movement of population to and from Cambridgeshire between 1851 and 1861', *Geographical Journal*, 101 (1943), 118–25; C. T. Smith, 'The movement of population in England and Wales in 1851 and 1861', *Geographical Journal*, 117 (1951), 200–10; R. Lawton, 'Population movements in the West Midlands, 1841–1861', *Geography*, 43 (1958), 164–77.
[5] W. L. Sargant, 'Inconsistencies of the English Census of 1861', *Journal of the Royal Statistical Society*, 28 (1865), 73–124.

figures are much lower than they should be and there is even less cause for concern about the relative standing of population totals returned at each date. Both Censuses were taken early in the year, and there is little possibility of seasonal migrations, such as that described by Williams,[1] upsetting the figures. In practice the precise boundaries of the parishes to which the statistics refer are difficult to determine for this period; a density distribution map must, therefore, be based upon the hundred as a unit. Fig. 30, a simple choropleth map, shows population density for the year 1801.

Fig. 31, showing population change between the first and second Censuses, in addition to the possibility of a more efficient enumeration in 1811 than in 1801, is complicated to some extent by small parish boundary changes. These can normally be traced in the Census of 1851, which gave the number of persons returned in each parish from 1801 onwards and attempted to account for any unusual fluctuations, but the problem is not serious as the statistical unit of the map is again the hundred.

Fig. 32, showing by hundreds the proportion of all houses uninhabited in 1801, and Fig. 33, showing houses abandoned in 1811, though constructed in the same way are not strictly comparable. The statistics used for the 1801 map include all uninhabited houses, irrespective of whether the houses were under construction or deserted. In 1811 Rickman distinguished between the two, but the figures are still difficult to handle. The number of houses building is a comparatively short-term index of prosperity and population growth; the number of houses abandoned, though an inverse measure of the same thing, may represent happenings over a much longer period, but for how long it is impossible to say. It may well be that many of the houses returned as uninhabited in 1801 were included in the 1811 returns. The comparison between the two figures which Rickman suggested is thus hard to interpret; it is much better to relate either or both to the total number of houses, as with the 1801 figures. There is another more practical reason for not following Rickman's suggestion when studying Wales: the number of houses under construction was too small in relation to the total number of houses to give significant results. A large number of parishes returned no houses building, and many more, less than five.

---

[1] M. I. Williams, 'Seasonal migrations of Cardiganshire harvest-gangs to the Vale of Glamorgan in the nineteenth century', *Ceredigion*, 3 (1957), 156–160.

The most satisfactory course for 1811 seems to be to examine the proportion of all houses abandoned.

The most difficult figures of all to treat in the early Censuses are those relating to occupations. Ignoring double counting, which was unimportant in Wales, there were two possible ways of answering the question circulated in 1801. In the first, active workers only were returned in the first two occupation categories; in the second, these categories also included workers' dependants. This means that the third category has variable and unrelated components and provides statistics which are virtually worthless, but the relative sizes of the first and second categories in each parish should be correct, supposing that in the parishes which returned dependants in the first two categories the average number of dependants to each agricultural worker did not differ greatly from the average number of dependants of those engaged in trade, manufacturing, and handicraft. It is this ratio between persons employed in agriculture and those employed in trade, manufacturing, and handicraft that has been shown in Fig. 34, though the basis of calculation is again the hundred and not the parish. In 1811 these problems did not arise because the number of families in each occupation category was required. Fig. 35 had been constructed in the same way as Fig. 34 so that direct comparisons may be made.

Population trends

The point has already been made that, in comparison with England, differences in population density from place to place in Wales in 1801 were unspectacular, but when looked at in detail the distribution map (Fig. 30) reveals some interesting variations. Many of the hundreds composing the upland core of Wales contained less than 50 persons per square mile, and these formed a continuous area of sparse population stretching from Snowdonia to the south Wales coalfield, roughly coextensive with the crop Highland Regions (Fig. 29). In the north-west, where the coast plain is narrow, some of the large hundreds adjoining the coast averaged less than fifty persons per square mile, but elsewhere the sparsely populated core gave way with decreasing altitude to hundreds which were more intensively settled (cf. Fig. 4). To the north-east the lowlands of Flintshire and Denbighshire formed the largest area of dense population in the country and to the north-west a number of hundreds in Anglesey and Caernarvonshire contained more than 100 persons per square mile; in fact, after Flintshire, Anglesey was

the most densely peopled county in Wales in 1801.[1] In the coastal hundreds of Cardiganshire and north Pembrokeshire, and in those along the mid Wales border population densities generally ranged

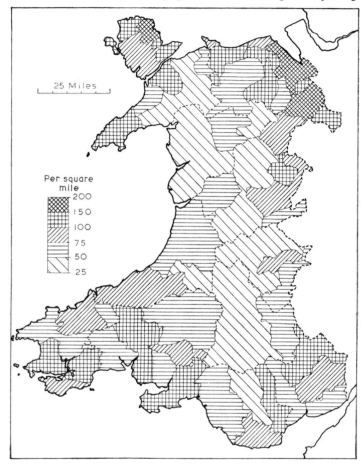

Fig. 30. Population density, 1801: by hundreds
(SOURCE: *Census 1801*.)

between 50 and 100 per square mile, but in south Wales, where large areas lie below 600 feet quite a number of hundreds returned more than 100 persons per square mile, though in no hundred did population density exceed 150 per square mile, as in five of the hundreds in

[1] H. C. Darby (ed.), *An historical geography of England before A.D. 1800* (Cambridge, 1948), 525.

north Wales. South Pembrokeshire, central Carmarthenshire, Gower
and the hinterland of Swansea, the south-east part of the Vale of
Glamorgan together with the hundred of Caerphilly stretching north

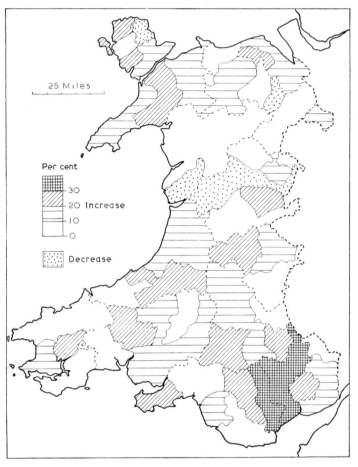

Fig. 31. Population change, 1801–1811: by hundreds
(SOURCE: *Census 1801, Census 1811.*)

to Merthyr Tudful, and northern Monmouthshire were the areas
with highest population densities.

Any map showing population density at this period gives necessarily a static, momentary picture of a most dynamic process.

Throughout the eighteenth century the growth and redistribution of population in Wales had gained momentum,[1] and after 1800 the changes which took place are clearly revealed by comparing the map for 1801 with those showing the distribution of population at later dates.[2] The differences in population density over the more limited period between 1801 and 1811 are shown in Fig. 31, which acts as a complement to Fig. 30 and represents population change during the Napoleonic wars. Unfortunately, unlike studies based upon later Censuses,[3] it is impossible from the statistics available to distinguish between changes resulting from the balance between births and deaths, that is, natural increase or decrease, and changes due to migration. It is possible though to relate local changes to the average for the whole of England and Wales: a population increase of roughly 15 per cent.

In Fig. 31 average hundreds are represented by the category showing population increases of 10–20 per cent. Of the hundreds which experienced more than average increases, the most impressive changes were in four at the eastern end of the south Wales coalfield (Fig. 17), where the iron industry was expanding rapidly.[4] The population of the Monmouthshire hundred of Gwynllwg, including Tredegar and Ebbw Vale, increased by 86 per cent over the ten years and that of the neighbouring hundreds of Abergavenny, Caerphilly and Kibbor by 30–40 per cent. Around the area where population had grown rapidly several other hundreds upon, or adjacent to, the coalfield experienced population increases of 20–30 per cent. Elsewhere in Wales hundreds in the same category were well scattered and frequently the increases were either very little above 20 per cent, as in south Cardiganshire, or had been contributed almost wholly by the major town of the hundred, as in the hundred of Swansea. It is notable that the counties which experienced population increases consistently above the average throughout the eighteenth century, Cardiganshire, Flintshire and Montgomeryshire,[5] were not outstanding in this respect between 1801 and 1811;

[1] Supra, 11.

[2] For population density, 1851, see W. Rees, *An historical atlas of Wales* (Cardiff, 1951), plate 70 (*b*); for population density, 1951, see E. G. Bowen (ed.), *Wales, a physical, historical, and regional geography* (London, 1957), 242.

[3] E.g. H. Carter, 'Population changes in Wales 1931 to 1951', *Geography*, 41 (1956), 126–9.

[4] Cf. plates 66 (*b*) and 66 (*c*) in W. Rees, op. cit.

[5] Supra, 11.

gradually there had been a change in the power of the coalfields, especially the south Wales coalfield, to attract population. The population increase in Glamorgan and Monmouthshire between 1801 and 1811 is a precursor of the even more spectacular increases which were to occur later in the century.

Much of north, central and west Wales experienced population increases at, or below, the average rate, and seven hundreds had fewer people in 1811 than in 1801.[1] This suggests that many of the dominantly rural areas had lost population by migration, though in absolute terms the losses should not be over-emphasized, as the population density in many of the hundreds was low. Some people went abroad,[2] but it is clear that large numbers moved to the growing industrial centres in south Wales and in England.

Figs. 32 and 33 suggest the areas most affected by migration loss. In 1801 the evidence leads to the conclusion that it was the hundreds near to the eastern part of the south Wales coalfield which contributed most to the movement at this early stage of industrial development. Nowhere outside the counties of Brecknock, Glamorgan, Monmouth and Radnor did the number of uninhabited houses exceed 5 per cent of the total number of houses in any hundred, but in the Brecknockshire hundreds of Crickhowell, Merthyr and Talgarth the figure approached 10 per cent. This short distance movement closely reflects the process outlined by Redford[3] of a migration by stages in which areas nearest to the growing industrial districts were affected first, and these in turn affected more distant areas in a 'complex wave-like motion'.[4] It is true that long distance movement, both seasonal and permanent, did take place but it was not nearly as important an element of population migration as in the second half of the century.[5] Around the north Wales coalfield, where population increases between 1801 and 1811 were generally

---

[1] In the hundred of Iâl, Denbighshire, it is possible that a boundary change produced the apparent loss; see *Census 1811*, 450, note (*o*).

[2] D. Williams, 'Some figures relating to emigration from Wales', *Bulletin of the Board of Celtic Studies*, 7 (1933–35), 396–415.

[3] A. Redford, *Labour migration in England, 1800–50* (Manchester, 1926), 160–1. The idea had been stated earlier in E. G. Ravenstein, 'The laws of migration', *Journal of the Royal Statistical Society*, 48 (1885), 167–235.

[4] See also A. H. John, *The industrial development of south Wales, 1750–1850* (Cardiff, 1950), 64–6.

[5] E. G. Bowen (ed.), op. cit., 235; A. E. Trueman, 'Population changes in the eastern part of the south Wales coalfield', *Geographical Journal*, 53 (1919), 418.

below the national average (Fig. 31), Fig. 32 shows that there was
no fringe of uninhabited houses comparable with that in south
Wales.

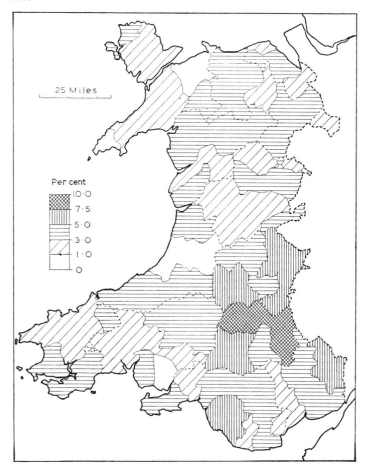

Fig. 32. Uninhabited houses, expressed as a percentage of all houses, 1801:
by hundreds

(SOURCE: *Census 1801.*)

The map showing the distribution of abandoned houses in 1811
(Fig. 33) confirms the pattern noted for 1801. In two hundreds only
in North Wales, Iâl and Nant Conwy, were more than 3 per cent
of the houses abandoned, yet around the south Wales coalfield

many hundreds contained high proportions of deserted houses.
Again the counties immediately to the north of the coalfield, Brecknockshire and Radnorshire, were most affected, but north-east

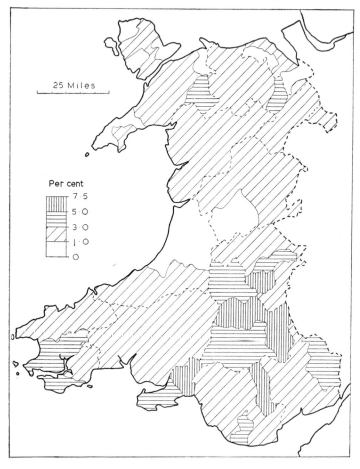

Fig. 33. Abandoned houses, expressed as a percentage of all houses, 1811:
by hundreds

(Source: *Census 1811.*)

Monmouthshire, the Vale of Glamorgan, Gower, and south
Pembrokeshire had also continued to lose people to the industrial
areas. In both 1801 and 1811 north Cardiganshire and the Severn
valley had few uninhabited houses; a reflection, probably, of the

combined effects of flourishing lead and woollen industries and the inaccessibility of the coalfields of north and south Wales. One anomalous feature of the map is provided by the large hundred of Caerphilly, Glamorgan, which, despite the expansion of the iron industry on the north crop of the coalfield, returned 6 per cent of its houses abandoned in 1811. As many of these were in parts of the Merthyr Tudful parish where coalmining was the dominant activity, for example the hamlet of Heolwermwd, it seems likely that it was the migratory nature of the coal industry at this period,[1] due to the small scale of each working, which led to local population movement and deserted houses.

Occupation structure

It is clear that many more were employed in agriculture than in trade, manufacturing, and handicraft in Wales in 1801 (Fig. 34). On average well over three-quarters of those in the first two categories of the occupation returns were employed in agriculture, a high proportion by any standards, and in many hundreds considerably more than three-quarters were so employed. For example, 93 per cent of those in the first two categories in the hundreds of Llifon and Malltraeth, western Anglesey, were agricultural workers, and in central Radnorshire the hundreds of Colwyn and Cefnllys returned over 96 per cent. The hundreds in which the proportion of those employed in agriculture to those employed in trade, manufacturing, and handicraft was appreciably smaller than in these examples fall broadly into three groups. First, there were hundreds containing sizeable towns or villages which acted as markets, secondly, hundreds which wholly, or in part, covered the coalfield industrial areas, and thirdly, hundreds in which the proportion of agricultural workers was low for various other reasons.

Usually in hundreds which contained large market centres there was, as might be expected, a great contrast in the ratio of agricultural to other workers between the town and the surrounding countryside. In a map of a larger scale than Fig. 34 these differences might have been illustrated but here it is possible only to note the effect upon the hundred occupation structure. Probably the most striking example is in the hundred of Isaled, Denbighshire, which included the small section of the Vale of Clwyd around the town of Denbigh, but the greater part of Mynydd Hiraethog south-westwards to the

[1] A. Redford, op. cit., 49.

headstreams of the river Conway. Though the population of Denbigh was less than one-fifth of the total population of the hundred the town contained nearly two-thirds of the people employed in trade,

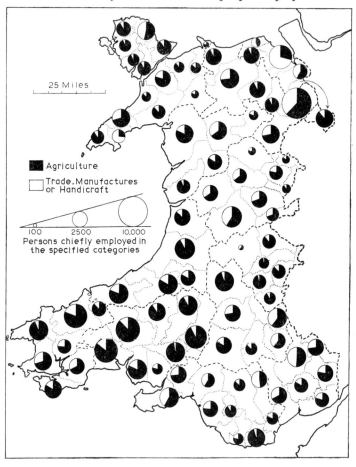

25 Miles

■ Agriculture.

□ Trade, Manufactures or Handicraft

100   2500   10,000
Persons chiefly employed in the specified categories

Fig. 34. Occupation structure, 1801: by hundreds
(SOURCE: *Census 1801.*)

manufacturing and handicraft. The result is that the average figure for agricultural workers in the hundred was reduced to 73 per cent of those returned in the first two categories. Other examples exist in the Brecknockshire hundred of Talgarth, where the town of Hay contained over half the people employed in trade, manufacturing, and handicraft, and in Monmouthshire, where the town of Monmouth contained nearly three-quarters of those so employed in the hundred of Skenfrith. The effect of the high proportion of non-agricultural workers in these towns was again to reduce the average figure for agricultural workers in the hundreds of Talgarth and Skenfrith to 62 per cent and 73 per cent respectively.

In the hundreds which covered the industrialized parts of the north and south Wales coalfields the proportion of agricultural workers to workers in trade, manufacturing, and handicraft was not only smaller but also generally more consistent throughout each hundred, as the industrial areas were already quite extensive. In north Wales the hundreds of Coleshill (29 per cent), Mold (58 per cent), Prestatyn (43 per cent) and Bromfield (63 per cent) have figures for agricultural workers which are reasonably representative of the parishes. In the north-east of the south Wales coalfield the same is true of the hundreds of Caerphilly (48 per cent) and Gwynllwg (68 per cent) but it is a generalization less applicable to hundreds such as Swansea (59 per cent), Llangyfelach (74 per cent), and Neath (60 per cent), where industry had been longer established and tended to be concentrated in larger settlements. In one sense these percentages of workers employed in agriculture on the coalfields are deceptively large. Workers in extractive industries should logically have been returned in the third occupation category; it is difficult to say whether this was done consistently, but it certainly seems to have been in the return for Heolwermwd, in the hundred of Caerphilly (I 25, II 442, III 4,559, population total 5,026). If coal miners could be introduced into the calculation then the percentage of workers employed in agriculture would decrease further. The same argument might also apply to north Cardiganshire, where lead mining was of considerable importance in 1801.

In yet other hundreds a wide range of activities diversified the occupation structure and diminished the importance of agricultural workers. In coastal hundreds such as Cafflogion (26 per cent) and Dinllaen (71 per cent) seaside parishes contained low proportions of agricultural workers; almost certainly a result of the local fishing industry. It is difficult to know in which occupation category fishermen were returned, but those engaged in ancillary activities, such as the harbour trades, would almost all have been placed in the second category. In Pembrokeshire the shipping industries reduced the figure for agricultural workers in the hundred of Rhos (71 per cent) which included the port of Haverfordwest (favoured because of its central position in the county) and Milford Haven, the packet port for southern Ireland. Associated with the export facilities of the port of Amlwch, on the north coast of Anglesey, and the copper deposits of Parys Mountain,[1] a smelting industry had grown up which differentiated the occupation structure of the hundred of Twrcelyn, from all others in the county. The returns for the parish of Llansilian, which extended to the foot of Parys Mountain (I 51, II 19, III 1,098, population total 1,168), suggest that here again workers engaged in extractive industry were returned in the third category. Those occupied in the widespread woollen industries of mid Wales clearly influenced the ratio of workers shown in Fig. 34. In most of the hundreds of the Severn valley, where the industry was best developed, workers employed in agriculture constituted appreciably less than three-quarters.

Fig. 35, showing the occupation structure for 1811, though based upon statistics not directly comparable with those used in Fig. 34, enables short period changes in the balance of occupations to be studied. There is no way of standardizing the absolute numbers of persons and families employed in agriculture, but the ratio, numbers in agriculture to numbers in trade, manufacturing, and handicraft in each hundred in 1801 and 1811, can be compared with reasonable certainty. It is possible that small differences between the two dates may not be significant of real changes but due to the inaccuracies of the returns; changes of less than 10 per cent between 1801 and 1811 in the percentage employed in agriculture are thus not considered. In a little over one-third of the hundreds small changes of this kind are revealed by a study of the two Censuses; in the remaining hundreds it is clear from a comparison of Figs. 34 and 35 that generally the proportion of agricultural workers fell over the ten years. Of a total number of 89 hundreds, 47 showed a relative decrease of 10 per cent or more in those employed in agriculture, while increases of the same order were shown by eight scattered hundreds only. Many of the hundreds in which the proportion of agricultural workers fell by 10 per cent or more were in or around the south Wales coalfield, and there was a close correlation between these and the areas shown to have been most affected by migration

[1] See A. H. Dodd, 'Parys Mountain during the industrial revolution, 1760–1840', *Transactions of the Anglesey Antiquarian Society and Field Club* (1926), 90–105.

in Figs. 32 and 33. In Brecknockshire, Carmarthenshire, Glamorgan, Monmouthshire, south Pembrokeshire and Radnorshire most hundreds experienced a large relative decline in agricultural workers,

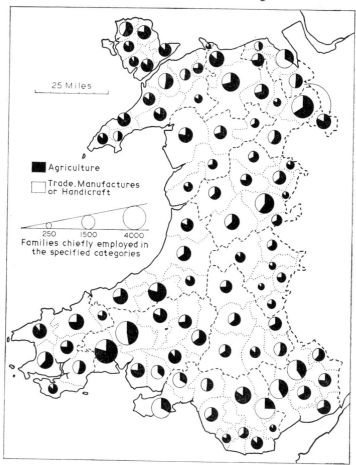

Fig. 35. Occupation structure, 1811: by hundreds
(SOURCE: *Census 1811.*)

and this was true not only of the fringing rural hundreds, such as Builth or Devynock in western Brecknockshire, which were losing farming population, but also of the industrialized hundreds, such as Caerphilly and Gwynllwg at the heart of the expansion where incoming rural workers were taking up employment in industry.

For the north Wales coalfield a comparison of Figs. 34 and 35 again corroborates the earlier evidence. In the upper Vale of Clwyd, it is true, there was a significant fall in the percentage employed in agriculture between 1801 and 1811, but there was no well-defined grouping of such hundreds on and around the coalfield as in south Wales. Of the four industrialized hundreds of Coleshill, Mold, Prestatyn and Bromfield, in one only did the proportion of agricultural workers decrease by 10 per cent and in two there were considerable increases.

In this treatment of the Censuses taken during the Napoleonic wars attention has been paid to population distribution, growth, migration, and composition but from only one of these aspects has it been possible to associate distinctive characteristics with any of the three major crop regions identified in Chapter 5. The population density of the Highland Regions was lower than for the Peripheral or Ingressive Regions but otherwise no clear differences were apparent. If small differences did exist between crop regions there are two reasons why these might be hidden. The first is that the statistical units upon which the distribution maps are based were large, and frequently straddled the boundaries of the crop regions; distinctiveness in adjacent regions would thus be merged. The second reason is that rural population in the decade under study was very sparse and any small differences resulting from agriculture were completely overshadowed by the influences of industrial activity; both industry in an agricultural setting, such as in Montgomeryshire, but more especially the great industries of the coalfields, the effects of which dominated Figs. 30–35.

III. CARTOGRAPHIC EVIDENCE

CHAPTER 7

ESTATE AND FARM PLANS

It is clear from an inspection of the estate and farm plans drawn during the Napoleonic wars that, unlike the material derived from the early Censuses, they fall into three fairly well defined categories: those which represent the Highland Regions, those which represent the Peripheral Regions, and those which represent the Ingressive Regions of Fig. 29. It is therefore possible to compare the major regions in much greater detail than in previous chapters and also to show to what extent the variations in cropland-use reflect different farming systems or landscape patterns.

Representative maps (Figs. 36–9) have been selected for each of the three major crop regions showing land-use, farm and field boundaries, and farm buildings. These plans rarely give information outside the boundary of the farm or estate; when holdings were fragmented no indication is given of what lay between the detached portions. To get a more complete picture of the countryside at this time it is necessary to know something of the area in which the plans are set; here the manuscript *Surveyors' Drawings* of the Ordnance Survey are of value, though a number of problems arise from their use. First, the dates of the official survey are sometimes much later than the dates of the farm plans. Secondly, the *Surveyors' Drawings* lack the detail of the farm surveys and this is emphasized in the Welsh sheets where no reliance can be placed in the field boundaries shown. A brief inspection suggests, and comparison with other maps confirms, that field boundaries were interpolated. Thirdly, no key exists to the maps and, though it is reasonable to suppose that the symbols are the same as those on later Ordnance Survey maps, it is difficult to know, for example, how the surveyors defined 'rough pasture'. Probably the sign representing 'rough pasture' signifies unenclosed grazing land; the rough pasture within the bounds of farms seems always to have been left unshaded.

The estate and farm plans selected as sample illustrations of conditions within the three major crop regions vary widely in accuracy, in their scales, and in the cartographic methods and symbols employed. In Figs. 36–9 this diverse material has been reproduced at the same scale and in a standard format. Each figure has two parts. In the left-hand section the material derived from the estate and farm plans has been shown in full and contours have been inserted from a modern map. In the right-hand section the same area has been redrawn from the *Surveyors' Drawings*. To facilitate comparisons between the two sections the farm boundaries from the left-hand side have also been shown on the right. As the 'common and waste' of the farm plans appears to be synonymous with the 'rough pasture' of the Ordnance Survey maps they have both been represented by the same shading.

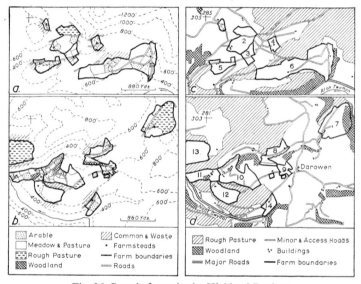

Fig. 36. Sample farms in the Highland Regions

a. Farms and their land-use in the parish of Cemais, Montgomeryshire, *c.* 1800 (SOURCE: N.L.W., Pen., Vol. 3.)

b. Farms and their land-use in the parish of Darowen, Montgomeryshire, *c.* 1800 (SOURCE: N.L.W., Pen., Vol. 3.)

c. The setting of the farms in *a*, 1832–4 (SOURCE: Ordnance Survey, *Surveyors' Drawings*, Sheets 332, 337.)

d. The setting of the farms in *b*, 1833–4 (SOURCE: Ordnance Survey, *Surveyors' Drawings*, Sheets 336–7.)

The Highland Regions

Fig. 36 represents in detail the agricultural landscape of the higher poor-grain parts of Montgomeryshire. The height of the land shown in the map is not excessive, in fact none of the sample farms had land much above 800 feet, but it is an area of great relief.[1] Streams such as Afon Twymyn and Nant Gwydol have entrenched themselves deeply into the hard Silurian rocks of the area, producing steep slopes and thin soils. With an annual rainfall of about 60 inches it is not surprising that in 1801 oats and rye were the typical crops in the parishes of Cemais and Darowen and that they occupied together 80 per cent of the cropland. Potatoes and barley were the next most important crops but less than 5 per cent of the cropland was devoted to wheat growing.

Roughly one-eighth of the area of the farms shown in Fig. 36 was in arable and it is characteristic of the time that some of the highest farmland was under the plough. The highest arable fields were on south-facing slopes (see farms 4, 8) and these, together with the limited areas of flatter land, appear to have been the most favoured. For example, in farm 6 the most northerly arable field was on a south slope, while the remaining arable lay in the broad east-west col through which the farm stretched. Some farms, of course, had no south-facing or flat land (5, 11), but these were exceptional. In general there was a tendency for the arable to be clustered around the farmstead, probably because both prospered best in the same physical setting; conditions which were not abundant in rough upland country.

While arable fields were among the smallest in each farm the fields under grass varied greatly in size between small paddocks and very large tracts. The smaller grass fields were generally disposed around the farmstead and were all classified as 'meadow and pasture'; with distance from the farmstead and with increasing altitude they tended to become bigger, and upon the exposed hilltops and higher northern slopes were the largest fields, often classified as 'rough' (2, 10). Comparatively little woodland occurred within the farm units, but the largest blocks again seem to have been on north slopes (8, 9, 10, 11).

The only information available in the farm documents for areas outside the farm boundaries was that sometimes adjoining land was marked as 'common' or 'waste'. This land has been indicated in Fig. 36 *a* and *b*, though it is shown to have been more extensive by the later Ordnance Survey maps. The wide distribution of common together with the dominance of grassland implies that the economy

[1] 1 : 25,000 O.S. sheet SH,80.

was based upon stock which was moved seasonally between lower and higher ground. This contention is supported by the evidence of place-names, which, though they cannot be regarded as proof because their origins pre-date the manuscript maps, are entirely consistent with the idea. For example farm 4 is called *Lluest-wen* and the hill to the south of farm 6 is *Fridd-fawr*. Both *lluest* and *fridd* are names which were linked closely with the seasonal movement of stock and their repeated occurrence in this area is suggestive.

As well as showing the distribution of the common and waste land Figs. 36 *c* and 36 *d* reveal that the sample farms are blocks of land at some time carved out of the common. Farm 4, at one period probably no more than a seasonal shepherd's hut but continuously occupied in 1800, is a clear example, and another is the farm to the north-east of it (Fig. 36 *c*). The piecemeal nature of the process is also shown. The common to the west of farm 1 disappeared between 1800 and 1832–34 and an intake from the common provided farm 4 with additional ground on its southern boundary. Similar encroachments into the common seem to have been made to the north-east of farm 6. These, and the more extensive enclosures resulting from parliamentary action, will be discussed further in the next chapter.

The picture which emerges in the Highland Regions is of farms, each with a little arable, concentrating upon animal husbandry. In the parishes of Cemais and Darowen all the fields were irregularly shaped and of varied size, but there was a noticeable correlation between size and the use to which they were put. Arable fields were small, on average 3·3 acres, and the largest was 10 acres. Fields under meadow and pasture were larger, with a mean size of 5·3 acres, but the range in size was also much greater. Fields under rough pasture averaged 30·1 acres and ranged from 5 to 50 acres. Farms varied in size from 3 acres (1) to 152 acres (6); the average was 49·9 acres.[1]

The Peripheral Regions

The Peripheral Regions (Fig. 29), those in which there was an intermixture of upland and lowland conditions, may be divided into two. To the west of the Highland Regions, where access from the

---

[1] These, and the following calculations of field and farm sizes, are based upon the available manuscript documents of a limited number of landowners. They rest upon two assumptions. First, that inaccuracies of field mensuration are more or less eliminated by averaging large numbers of fields, and secondly that tenants rented no land from other owners.

east was restricted, was the extensive OB region covering most of Cardiganshire, Carmarthenshire, north-west Merioneth, and north Pembrokeshire. To the east of the Highland Regions and along parts of the south Wales coast were the remaining Peripheral Regions, WO, WOB, and WOBPe, all showing wheat to have been an important crop and hence signifying contact with lowland England. Representative manuscript plans are available for both these subdivisions and they are therefore considered separately.

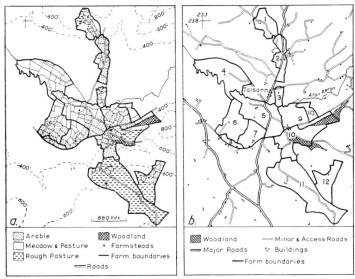

Fig. 37. Sample farms in the western Peripheral Regions

a. Farms and their land-use in the parishes of Llanfihangel Ystrad and Trefilan, Cardiganshire, 1799–1800 (Source: N.L.W., Vol. 7.)

b. The setting of the farms, 1811–19 (Source: Ordnance Survey, *Surveyors' Drawings*, Sheets 186, 308.)

Fig. 37 shows in detail a number of farms in the parishes of Llanfihangel Ystrad and Trefilan, Cardiganshire, to the west of the heartland core of the country. Though the height of the farmland shown is not very different from that in Cemais and Darowen the country is less rugged.[1] Afon Aeron, a more mature stream than any in Fig. 36, has developed with the aid of tributary streams a wide valley at this point; consequently there is much flat land, and steep slopes occur only in the extreme east and north of the map. In these

[1] 1 : 25,000 O.S. sheet SN,55.

conditions, and with an annual rainfall of 45 inches, oats and barley were both typical, though not equally important, crops. In both parishes oats occupied 59 per cent and barley 28 per cent of the cropland. Again less than 5 per cent of the cropland was devoted to wheat.

The most evident contrast between farms shown in Fig. 37 and those of the Highland Regions is in the amount of arable land. Here, in a representative sample of country extending across the Aeron valley, one-third of the farmland was in arable. In an area of such moderate slopes the form of the ground was a less important determinant of arable working and soil drainage seems to have been the most important factor. Few of the arable fields were on the valley bottom, but they stretched up the valley sides to both north and south to a height of over 600 feet. In a number of instances the arable fields abutted the rough grazing (1, 10, 11, 12).

The meadow and pasture fields were far more uniform in size than in the Highland Regions and very like the arable fields. Meadow and pasture was associated closely with the valley bottoms, and the fields bordering the Aeron and its left bank tributaries were characteristically under grass. Farm 4, which lay wholly upon the river flood-plain, had no arable. The rough pasture, as one might expect, was upon the higher land where it occurred in large fields. There was little woodland within the farms. All the wood shown in Fig. 37 a was in farm 10, where two large blocks occupied the steepest slopes in the area. A typical land-use traverse from valley bottom to hilltop would thus show meadow and pasture adjacent to the river, arable on the valley side and, on the higher ground, rough pasture. When considering parishes this characteristic association would have some validity but, as can be seen from Fig. 37, only one farm (12) of all those shown exhibited these 'typical' traits. No better demonstration could be found of the hazards, already mentioned,[1] of relying wholly upon parish summaries.

The manuscript maps of the Ordnance Survey, drawn between ten and twenty years later, add little to the information of the farm plans. The absence of common is confirmed and the accessibility of most farms to main roads is shown; the north-west–south-east main road was the Lampeter–Aberaeron turnpike (Fig. 3). But the principal value of the maps is that they disclose the dense scatter of settlement over the whole area.

[1] Supra, 57.

The farming system in the parishes of Llanfihangel Ystrad and Trefilan is less evident from the documents available than that in the Highland Regions, but it is clear that generally animals were not as important. In farms with large grazing areas (4, 11, 12) the end product would have been sheep or cattle but in many farms (2, 3, 8, 9) the head of stock must have been low, and cash cropping of importance. As in the Highland Regions fields were irregularly shaped but a statistical analysis of land-use and related field sizes reveals a number of contrasts. Arable fields were only slightly bigger, averaging 3·7 acres, with only three outside the range 1–6 acres, but meadow and pasture fields were much smaller and more consistent in size than those shown in Fig. 36, on average 4·1 acres. Fields under rough pasture averaged 76·2 acres, but with so few, this figure is much influenced by the 214-acre stretch of farm 11. Farms ranged from 13 acres (3) to 232 acres (11) and the average size was 96·1 acres.

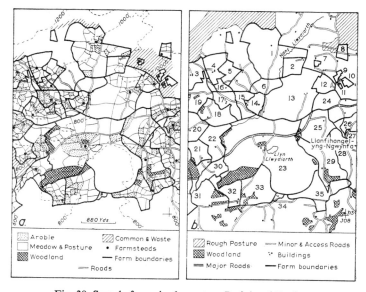

Fig. 38. Sample farms in the eastern Peripheral Regions

a. Farms and their land-use in the parish of Llanfihangel-yng-Ngwynfa, Montgomeryshire, *c.* 1800 (SOURCE: N.L.W., Gls. 7, RM, B76.)

b. The setting of the farms, 1829–33 (SOURCE: Ordnance Survey, *Surveyors' Drawings,* Sheets 328, 330, 332.)

Fig. 38 covers nearly one-half of the enclosed area of the large parish of Llanfihangel-yng-Ngwynfa, Montgomeryshire, and the farms shown represent those of the Peripheral Regions to the east of the highland core. From the point of view of elevation the area is much more marginal to conditions in the Highland Regions than the Cardiganshire example; farmland ranges from 600 feet in the south of the map to well over 1,100 feet in the north-west. But the streams which drain the area, small left bank tributaries of the Vyrnwy, have smooth cross-profiles resulting in a subdued relief with few steep slopes.[1] The parish lies in the rain-shadow of the Welsh Massif and consequently the annual rainfall of 45–50 inches is lower than might be expected at this height. The crop combination index of the parish is WOB. Oats was the most important crop occupying 55 per cent of the cropland. Wheat, significantly in second place, occupied 20 per cent and barley 16 per cent of the cropland.

The marginal nature of the area is demonstrated by the fact that one-sixth of the enclosed land was in arable, roughly half that in OB the region of Cardiganshire and other, more lowland, WOB parishes, but more than in the OR region to the south-west. Arable land was well distributed over the area; it ranged from the lowest land to all but the very highest, and several fields were at 1,000 feet (1, 3, 4). The southern slopes were again preferred but there is also a noticeable tendency for arable to appear on the floors of the broader valleys. Fields were everywhere small and irregularly shaped except in the largest farm of the area, Llwydiarth Hall (23), where five large arable fields were grouped around the farmstead. As the centre of the local squirearchy, and astride the only turnpike road of the district (Fig. 3), it is probable that here less traditional methods, more in accord with those of the eastern lowlands, were employed, and these would have distinguished the farm from those around. This prompts the speculation that much of the wheat may have been grown on this one farm; such was the method by which new agricultural ideas and systems diffused into Wales at this period.

The fields shown as meadow and pasture were variable in size. The document from which Fig. 38 was derived showed no rough grazing land, but it is most likely that many of the large meadow and pasture fields in the high parts of farms (1, 4, 23) were occupied by the coarser grasses. Elsewhere meadow and pasture was ubiquitous

[1] 1 : 25,000 O.S. sheet SJ,01.

except upon the few steep slopes which were invariably devoted to woodland. In only one instance to the north of Llwydiarth Hall (23) was an area of woodland not associated with a steep slope, and here it probably had amenity value.

The pressure to enclose the upland commons is as evident in Llanfihangel-yng-Ngwynfa as in Cemais and Darowen. There were small squatter enclosures (7–11) upon the common in the north-east of the map, and in the north-west the highest fields of farm 3 were marked on the original manuscript as recent intakes from the mountain sheepwalk. A comparison of the two sections of Fig. 38, the one for the year 1800 and the other surveyed between 1829 and 1833, gives further evidence. The two small commons completely surrounded by farmland, lying south of farms 4 and 21 respectively, disappeared over the period, and the commons in the north-east and north-west of the map were reduced in size. The enclosures were probably the result of the act of 1811.[1]

In many ways the area shown in Fig. 38 was marginal between the Peripheral and Highland Regions, and if a separate crop combination index could have been calculated for the northern third of the map it is certain that it would have been O. Such an example has advantages; in this instance because it has demonstrated the extreme conditions in which the WOB crop combination occurred, and has shown, far more clearly than in a lower area, the process of agricultural reform. The marginal nature of the area is reflected in average sizes of fields and farms. Arable fields, with a mean acreage of 2·1, were smaller than any so far encountered in these examples. Meadow and pasture fields averaged 4·1 acres, the same figure as in the OB region, but if the large upland fields are considered as rough pasture, then the average would be reduced and would fall midway between those of the OR and OB regions. Farm size is again variable ranging from the tiny encroachments on the common of a few acres (7, 11) to Llwydiarth Hall farm (23); the mean size was 53·5 acres.

The Ingressive Regions

Fig. 39 shows a number of farms in the parishes of Diserth, Rhuddlan, and Rhyl, at the northern end of the Vale of Clwyd where the broad rift valley gives way to the north Wales coast plain.

[1] 51 Geo. III, c. 87; see also A. D. Rees, *Life in a Welsh countryside* (Cardiff, 1950), 18–20.

It is an area of lowland, almost wholly below 100 feet, drained by the Clwyd and its sluggish tributaries. The solid geology of the area, mainly Triassic sandstone (Fig. 17), is masked by a variety of superficial deposits. Fortunately a soil map on the 1 : 63,360 scale has recently been published.[1] This shows that in the extreme west of Fig. 39 poorly drained gley soils and immature alluvium border the Clwyd, but in the centre and east brown earths are developed upon

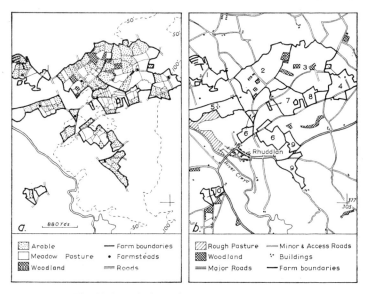

Fig. 39. Sample farms in the Ingressive Regions

a. Farms and their land-use in the parishes of Diserth, Rhuddlan, and Rhyl, Flintshire, 1810 (SOURCE: N.L.W., Br. II.)

b. The setting of the farms, 1819–21 (SOURCE: Ordnance Survey, *Surveyors' Drawings*, Sheet 309.)

mixed drift of Silurian and Triassic origin. These soils are as varied as their parent materials and, even with an annual rainfall little over 25 inches, range from the excessively drained to the gleyed, from soils with a high to those with a low base status. None of the three parishes shown in Fig. 39 has an extant 1801 return but a few miles to the south lie Bodfari and Denbigh, both of which have a crop combination index of WB. In these parishes wheat and barley

---

[1] Soil Survey of England and Wales, sheet 95 (Rhyl).

together occupied more than 70 per cent of the cropland. In St. Asaph and Gwaunysgor, adjacent parishes to the south-west and north-east, 65 per cent of the cropland was devoted to wheat and barley. In Bodfari and Gwaunysgor more than 6 per cent of the cropland was in turnips and rape.

It is clear from the map (Fig. 39) that over half the land shown was under arable. This land was widely distributed and in all farms, except the two smallest (8, 10) where the acreage in arable was low, similar proportions of the farm areas were under the plough. The gley soils and alluvium to the west of the town of Rhuddlan were unsuited to arable working. For example, the most westerly and largest field of farm 5 was in grass, and a complete farm, wholly upon the gley soils to the north-west of farm 1 but off the present map, had no arable. Upon the varied brown earths in the centre and east of the map there is no perceptible association between soil series and the distribution of arable fields, but had the manuscript maps shown crops then a relationship with soil texture and drainage would probably have been apparent.

The meadow and pasture fields were as uniform in size and shape as those under arable. With the exception of the grassland upon the soils with impeded drainage, there was no evident correlation with soil type. No rough pasture or common grazing was shown on the estate plans but the Ordnance Survey map, drawn between nine and eleven years later, shows rough pasture upon the alluvium flanking the Clwyd. Woodland was abundant, but confined to the two largest farms (2, 3). There seems to have been a decrease in the acreage of woodland between 1810 and 1819.

From all points of view the farmland shown in Fig. 39 is distinguishable from that of the previous samples. The fields were more symmetrically disposed; they were larger but also more uniform in size. Arable fields averaged 5·7 acres and meadow and pasture fields had an average acreage of 5·4, both figures larger than in any of the other regions. The range in the sizes of farms was also much less and the average acreage was 126·5, again the highest figure yet encountered. One characteristic of the farms in this area was their fragmentation. Farms 1, 4, 6, 7, 9, and 10 had detached portions and farm 7 had a field within its boundary belonging to another owner. The existence of unfenced strips in arable fields of farm 1 belonging to four different owners, together with additional evidence of working in common arable fields for the parishes of Rhuddlan, Gwaunysgor, and St. Asaph,[1] suggests that this dispersed pattern was the result of unorganized, piecemeal enclosure of open fields and waste.

The arable strips within farm 1 introduce the topic of open fields, another typically lowland feature of the Welsh agricultural scene, but one which was, either actually or in remnant form, distributed far more widely than the Ingressive Regions in 1801. Recent work has given a fairly clear picture of the development and spread of open fields in Wales. In many parts of the country, as a result of the Anglo–Norman colonization, manorial feudalism had been grafted onto the Welsh tribal system. It is difficult to determine the distribution of manors in Wales, partly because of the lack of certain evidence but also because it is sometimes hard to decide, especially in the north-west where conquest was late and the native tradition strong, whether systems so different from their English models were, in fact, manors at all. Fig. 40, derived from the work of Rees, shows the distribution of manors in the fourteenth century and is the best available map. After the establishment of a manor open field agriculture was not introduced automatically. The application of the Anglo–Norman agricultural system in Wales was very flexible, depending upon both local physical and political conditions; often manorial cultivation did not take place.[2] Again, it must be remembered that open arable fields had also existed under the Welsh tribal code and a few vestiges still remain.[3] But generally speaking, it is the English open field patterns and nomenclature that are most evident in the historical sources and in the field.

The Anglo–Norman open field system was diffused westward from the English lowlands along the routeways provided by the north and south coast plains and the major river valleys. In north Wales it was to be found well dispersed along the Flintshire coast, in the Vale of Clwyd,[4] and as far west as Caernarvonshire, where bond vills of the

---

[1] D. Sylvester, 'Settlement patterns in rural Flintshire', *Flintshire Historical Society Publications*, 15 (1954–55), 22, 34.

[2] W. Rees, *South Wales and the March, 1284–1415* (Oxford, 1924), 131.

[3] E.g. G. R. J. Jones, 'Some medieval rural settlements in north Wales', *Transactions and Papers, 1953*, Institute of British Geographers, 19 (1954), 51-72; idem., 'The pattern of settlement on the Welsh border', *Agricultural History Review*, 8 (1960), 66–81; idem., 'Medieval open fields and associated settlement patterns in northwest Wales', in X. de Planhol (ed.), *Géographie et Histoire Agraires* (Nancy, 1959), 313–28; idem., 'The tribal system in Wales: a re-assessment in the light of settlement studies', *Welsh History Review*, 1 (1961), 111–32.

[4] S. Sylvester, op. cit., 6–42.

'maerdref-demesne' type were adapted to the manorial system.[1] Around Wrexham, Denbighshire, an Anglo-Norman type of administration was gradually superimposed upon an earlier open field

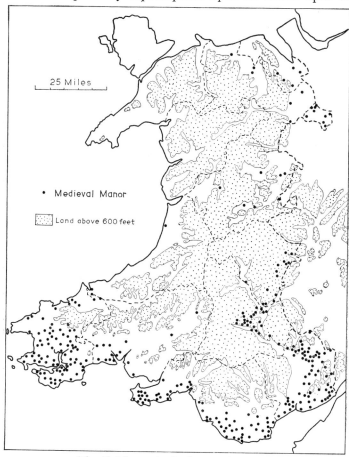

Fig. 40. Manors in the fourteenth century
(SOURCE: W. Rees, *An historical atlas of Wales* (Cardiff, 1951), Pl. 47.)

system.[2] In mid-Wales there is evidence that working in common fields spread along the Severn and other valleys[3] but in south

[1] W. O. Williams, *Tudor Gwynedd* (Caernarvon, 1958), 29.
[2] G. A. Usher in A. H. Dodd (ed.), *A history of Wrexham, Denbighshire* (Wrexham, 1957), 16–26; see also A. N. Palmer and E. Owen, *A history of ancient tenures of land in north Wales and the Marches* (Frome, 1910).
[3] E.g. E. G. Bowen, 'A map of the Trehelig common fields', *Montgomeryshire Collections*, 41 (1929–30), 163–8; D. Sylvester, 'The rural landscape of eastern Montgomeryshire', *Montgomeryshire Collections*, 54 (1955), 3–26.

Wales, where the coast plain is wide and occupation from the east was relatively easy, there are many examples. Davies has demonstrated the existence of open field types of agriculture in all the counties of south Wales from Monmouthshire to Pembrokeshire and also northwards along the shore of Cardigan Bay.[1]

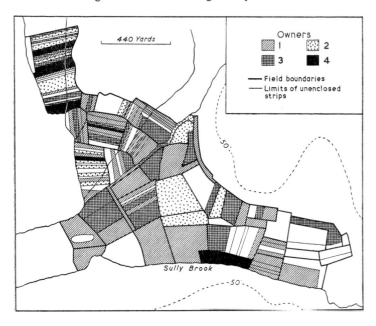

Fig. 41. Land ownership in an area of common meadows, St. Andrews Major, Glamorgan, 1798. The holdings of the four principal owners are shown.

(Source: Glamorgan Record Office, D/DWe 2; Tithe Redemption Commission, 51, 3.)

It is difficult to estimate how many of these fields were open at the time of the Napoleonic wars. The incumbents who completed the Acreage Returns of 1801 did not once mention open fields in Wales, and yet some of the parishes returned, such as Laugharne, Carmarthenshire, Rhosili, Glamorgan, and Undy, Monmouthshire, still contained open fields when the maps of the Tithe Redemption

[1] M. Davies, 'Field patterns in the Vale of Glamorgan', *Transactions of the Cardiff Naturalists' Society*, 84 (1954–55), 5–14; idem., 'Common lands in south-east Monmouthshire', ibid., 85 (1955–56), 5–15; idem., 'The open fields of Laugharne', *Geography*, 40 (1955), 169–77; idem., 'Rhosili open field and related south Wales field patterns', *Agricultural History Review*, 4 (1956), 80–96.

Commissioners were drawn at about 1840.[1] More important is that
the areas where the manorial agricultural system had operated
provided such a great contrast with the remaining areas of Wales.
The system was alien in origin; the method of farming and the
whole structure of society was different. The field patterns which it
contributed to the landscape were, of course, the characteristic long,
narrow strips. In the parishes of Laugharne, Rhosili, and Undy
these are still evident at the present.[2] The ownership pattern, where
extensive consolidation had not subsequently taken place, was fragmented. A contemporary example is afforded by a manuscript map
of parts of the parish of St. Andrews Major, Glamorgan, where
meadowland was held according to manorial custom (Fig. 41).
From the holdings of the four principal landowners the dispersed
nature of the property of each can be seen. In the large field in the
north-west of the map, for example, the four owners, together with
a number of others, held unfenced strips. There is no evidence that,
as sometimes happened, one occupier rented adjacent plots. In the
tithe map and apportionment of 1840 these same strips were held
by seven separate owners and occupied by eight different tenants.[3]
Fig. 41 thus serves as an illustration of the Anglo–Norman type of
tenure and also as a reminder that, though the examples usually
quoted are of open arable fields, common meadow was sometimes
organized on this basis.[4]

[1] See also P. Flatrès, *Géographie rural de quatre contrées Celtiques* (Rennes, 1957),
Fig. 44 (facing 412).
[2] See 1 : 25,000 O.S. sheets SN,31 ; SS,48 ; ST,48. The general distribution of
strip fields at the present is shown in P. Flatrès, op. cit., 398.
[3] Tithe Redemption Commission, 51, 3.
[4] For further examples see M. Davies (1954–55), op. cit., 12–14.

CHAPTER 8

ENCLOSURE AWARDS

SLATER, in an early paper, calculated that in the English Midlands a high proportion of the total acreage of each county was enclosed by act of parliament in the eighteenth and nineteenth centuries.[1] In the county of Northampton common fields covering over 50 per cent of the area were enclosed by act and in the counties of Bedford, Huntingdon, Oxford, and Rutland over 45 per cent of the area was affected. In Wales the effects of the enclosure movement upon agriculture were not as pronounced.[2] Far less land remained unenclosed, and of that, very little was common arable. Most of the land involved was rough grazing or waste upon which local farmers were allowed to depasture stock; areas which, at some previous period, were considered unworthy of enclosed working. No great change in practice resulted comparable with that in the Midlands where, upon enclosure, many farmers forsook the arable economy for pastoralism, but in detail parliamentary enclosure in Wales led to a re-organization of farming systems.

Land of four kinds in Wales was liable to enclosure: the upland moors, coastal waste, lowlying marsh and valley land, and open arable fields. During the Napoleonic wars the first of these was by far the most important. Fig. 8 has already shown, in a general way, the areas affected by enclosure, examples will illustrate the processes.

The upland moors

There were numerous examples during the Napoleonic wars of the enclosing of upland moors by act of parliament. Easily the most spectacular of these was an act which authorised the enclosure of 40,000 acres on Fforest Fawr, Brecknockshire, in 1808,[3] but in Montgomeryshire eleven years earlier the enclosure of a comparable area had been sanctioned by two acts.[4] Fig. 42, derived from one of the resulting awards in 1807, shows the enclosure of a small part of the parish of Ceri, and serves as an example of this type. One enclosure award dealing with upland moor in the manor of Arwystli,

---

[1] G. Slater, 'The inclosure of common fields considered geographically', *Geographical Journal*, 29 (1907), 38.
[2] Supra, 31.
[3] 48 Geo. III, c. 73.
[4] 36 Geo III, c. 17; 37 Geo. III, c. 115.

west Montgomeryshire, has already been fully documented by Thomas.[1] Though the operation of awards varied from place to place, and though the Arwystli award is dated 1826, it is interesting to see how closely it was paralleled by the enclosure in Ceri.

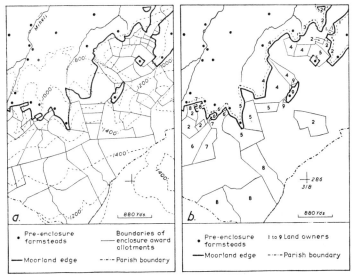

Fig. 42. Parliamentary enclosure of upland waste and common in the parish of Ceri, Montgomeryshire, 1807

a. Enclosure award allotments. No field boundaries are shown in the areas already enclosed.

b. The ownership pattern. The allotments to owners whose land adjoined the former common are shown.

(SOURCE: N.L.W., Montgomeryshire County Council Deposit, 14R.)

Before enclosure, the system which generally operated on upland commons was that neighbouring farmers were allowed to depasture stock, the numbers being determined by the animals they could feed on their enclosured farms during the winter. Through time encroachments were made on the common land.[2] Farmers whose land adjoined the unenclosed areas often increased their enclosed acreage by gradually moving out their boundary fences into the

---

[1] J. G. Thomas, 'The distribution of the commons in part of Arwystli at the time of enclosure', *Montgomeryshire Collections*, 54 (1955), 27–33; idem., 'Some enclosure patterns in central Wales', *Geography*, 42 (1957), 25–36. A summary of the proceedings leading to the enclosure of yet other upland moors, in the north-eastern part of Mynydd Hiraethog, is given in W. Ll. Davies, 'The Henllan enclosure award', *Bulletin of the Board of Celtic Studies*, 9 (1937–39), 247–71, 367.

[2] J. G. Thomas (1957), op. cit., 27–31.

common. Other instances exist of enclosures, sometimes very large, being made away from the existing farm. Provided these were carried out by established landlords or their tenants they often became, in fact or by implication, legal holdings. It was the smaller encroachments made by landless squatters which were frequently declared illegal by the manorial court leet. These were a result of the *tŷ-unnos* tradition in which it was popularly believed, quite mistakenly, that if a cottage could be erected on the common in one night, the builder had a legal right to the dwelling and to the land within one axe-throw in every direction. In Fig. 42 there is evidence of each of these types of encroachment. It is likely that the land of owner 5 was extended into the common from the farmstead at about 1,100 feet southwards along the floor of a small valley to the height of 1,200 feet where, at the time of parliamentary enclosure, he owned another farmstead. Owner 8, clearly a prominent landowner judging by the allotments he subsequently received in the south of the parish, held a few acres of land in the west of the map detached from the rest of his estate which seem to have been an intake from the common. Finally, small-scale squatter encroachments are possibly represented by the holdings of owners 5 and 9 in the north-east. Both were at over 1,000 feet and well clear of the moorland edge, though at the time of parliamentary enclosure they were in the hands of large landowners. At this period they were probably used as stock enclosures into which animals, grazing upon the common, could be collected when needed. A building, quite close to that owned by 5, is still today known as 'Shepherd's Lodge'.

The result of piecemeal enclosure and encroachment was that the moorland edge developed as a very irregular line. As at Arwystli[1] it lay in Ceri at approximately 1,000 feet at the beginning of the nineteenth century, but there were considerable variations, apparently governed by physical conditions. In the sheltered valley in the centre of Fig. 42 enclosed land reached 1,200 feet, but on the steep and exposed north-west slope in the north of the map the moorland edge fell below 800 feet. The picture was further complicated by the isolated encroachments on the common and by small pieces of common, like that in the north-east of the map, which were completely surrounded by enclosed land and which lay below the general line of the moorland edge. It was from this

[1] J. G. Thomas (1955), op. cit., 29.

irregular base that the commissioners appointed by the enclosure act divided the unenclosed land between the lord of the manor, the Earl of Powis, and those who could prove rights of common.

It is clear from Fig. 42 that the allotments made by the commissioners in the parish of Ceri were distinctive. The units were large, many of those in the map being over half a mile in length, and the boundaries were generally straight, though rarely were the units rectangular as they often were in less rugged country. Sometimes it is difficult to know, when studying enclosure awards, if the units shown in the maps were intended to be fields or whether they were ownership blocks. In the Ceri award there seems no doubt that the boundaries shown are field boundaries: directions were given about individual responsibilities for building hedges and fences, and frequently one owner was allotted adjacent plots. It is true that in a few instances the boundaries were either never built, or were not laid out as directed; a point which can be verified in the field or by a comparison with the relevant 1 : 25,000 Ordnance Survey map.[1] But generally the terms of the award were followed and there resulted the large sheep runs, shown in Fig. 42, stretching up to the crest of the hills at over 1,400 feet. These must have provided a great contrast with the typical small fields of the longer-enclosed areas (cf. Figs. 36–8).

Thomas, in his study of the enclosing of the commons of Arwystli, identified four patterns of ownership which followed the award.[2] All of these are illustrated in Fig. 42. First, blocks of land were given to landowners whose enclosed farms did not abut the common. All the newly enclosed land not numbered in Fig. 42 b belongs to this class. In the maps of the Ceri award, only the names of the owners of land adjoining the common were given; it is thus impossible to know where the farms of the other owners lay, but inevitably their post-enclosure holdings must have become fragmented, with sheep runs detached from the farmstead and the smaller fields in which the animals were wintered. Secondly, owners who held land, detached from their main farms, which at some time had been enclosed from the common received allotments on the basis of this provided that the commissioners could be satisfied about the legality of the holdings. Owner 8, in the west of the map, received a small strip of land adjoining his already enclosed encroachment, though in the

[1] Sheet SO,18.
[2] J. G. Thomas (1957), op. cit., 32–3.

south of the map he was awarded three very large units, clearly claimed on the basis of another extensive holding. Thirdly, those owners whose land adjoined the common received allotments, as far as was practical, continuous with their farms; that is, their upper boundaries were legally moved out into the common. Owners 1, 2, 4, 5, 6, and 7 (Fig. 42 *b*) provide examples of this type, but both 2 and 7 also received detached blocks: it is unfortunate that the award does not give the reason. Lastly, the squatters encroachments, usually considered by the commissioners to be legal if they were more than twenty years old, were allocated adjacent plots of land. Both the small enclosures owned by 5 and 9 are examples. No trace exists of similar encroachments which had been declared illegal, probably because any which existed would have been absorbed into new land units. Sometimes the commissioners allowed illegal squatters to buy their holdings, thus giving them legal possession,[1] but there is no evidence of this in Ceri.

The major effect of parliamentary enclosure upon the ownership pattern in upland areas was to produce estates which were much less compact than those produced in Midland England. Consolidated farms and estates were equally as desirable as in the Midlands but the obstacles facing the commissioners were even greater than in the enclosing of the open arable fields. Some fragmented holdings were inevitable, but in other instances where the creation of compact blocks was theoretically possible the problems presented by the irregular moorland edge, combined with the difficulties of apportioning fairly a rugged exposed common, seem to have proved too much for the appointed commission.

The coastal waste

Next in importance to the parliamentary acts which enclosed the upland moors during the Napoleonic wars were those which led to the enclosing and reclamation of coastal common and waste. One such act in 1810 authorized the enclosure of the sandy waste, marsh, and mud flats of Morfa Dyffryn, the littoral between Barmouth and Harlech, Merioneth.[2] The parishes of Llanbedr and Llanenddwyn occupied the widest part of this low coastal strip and it is the enclosure award for these which has been represented in Fig. 43. The map has been derived not from the award itself but from an undated, though certified, copy of the allocations held in the Public

[1] J. G. Thomas (1955), op. cit., 32.
[2] 50 Geo. III, c. 56.

Record Office. Morgan, who worked on the original award, gives its date as 1836.[1] Writing twelve years after the award was issued, Lewis commented that a considerable portion of the parish of Llanenddwyn had been brought into a good state of cultivation.[2]

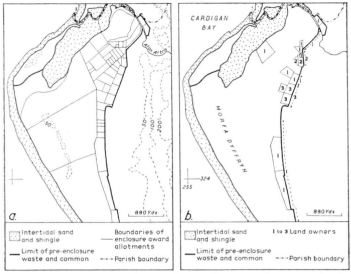

Fig. 43. Parliamentary enclosure of coastal waste and common in the parishes of Llanbedr and Llanenddwyn, Merioneth, 1836

  a. Enclosure award allotments. No field boundaries are shown in the areas already enclosed.

  b. The ownership pattern. The allotments to three selected owners are shown.

(Source: P.R.O., MP E, 118.)

The physical character of the land shown in Fig. 43 is fairly typical of many such areas around the coast of Wales. Here a dominantly northward longshore drift of beach material has led to the growth of a geologically Recent coast plain, two miles wide at its broadest but tapering away in the north and south to a few hundred yards in width. The Recent deposits are of two kinds. Behind the sand and shingle beach, and stretching inland for between half and three-quarters of a mile, lies a belt of dunes. The crest of these low, unstable sandhills is marked in Fig. 43 by the 50-foot

[1] C. Morgan, 'The effect of parliamentary enclosure on the landscape of Caernarvonshire and Merioneth', unpublished thesis, M.Sc., University of Wales, 1959, Fig. 23.

[2] S. Lewis, *A topographical dictionary of Wales* (London, 1848), II, *sub nom.* Llanenddwyn, 14.

contour. Further inland and again lying roughly parallel with the coast is a belt of marshy river alluvium; a result of infilling behind the sand bulwark by small streams flowing westward off the Harlech dome into Cardigan Bay. These streams have been diverted northwards by the drift of sediment and have become tributaries of Afon Artro, the major river of the area which, though also deflected northward, has maintained its course to the sea. To the east of the area of river alluvium at roughly the 50-foot contour the Recent deposits give way to hard rocks of Cambrian age.

It is difficult to determine the exact way in which the common was used before enclosure. Probably, as in Ceri, neighbouring landlords, certainly those who were later awarded allotments, were allowed to depasture stock upon the areas which supported grass, but there is some evidence that there was not the same pressure upon the common as there was in the uplands. No sign exists in Fig. 43 of the small squatter holdings so characteristic of the upland moors and the regularity of the boundary of the common, contrasting markedly with the moorland edge in Fig. 42, suggests that there had been no recent encroachments by owners or tenants whose land adjoined the common. A study of the settlement of the two parishes in the field lends support to these statements. In the area which was common land before 1836 there is no trace of buildings which pre-date the enclosure award, but in the enclosed area the distribution of farmsteads is very clear. The general height of the belt of marshy river alluvium is 20 feet above sea level; farmsteads were invariable above 25 feet and to the east of this belt. Contemporary plans for ten farms in the parishes of Llanaber, Llanbedr, Llanddwywe, and Llanenddwyn[1] throw further light on the local agricultural system and point to reasons for the lack of encroachment. The typical holding in the area was elongated east to west and straddled the boundary between the Cambrian rocks and the alluvium, roughly half of which had been enclosed before the enclosure act was passed. The farmstead generally lay at a height of 50 feet at about the centre of the enclosed land. To the west were the larger fields on the alluvium, generally under meadow and pasture, and to the east there were smaller fields, mainly in arable. On the higher ground beyond the arable some of the bigger farms held large blocks of rough pasture. The acreage under arable almost always exceeded that under meadow and pasture and sometimes occupied over half

[1] N.L.W., Deposit F. Ll. Griffith, Caernarvon (1800).

the farm area. It seems therefore that holdings in this part of Merioneth were less dependent upon the common grazing land than those in the uplands. The proportion of arable was higher (cf. Figs. 36 and 37) which probably meant, at this period and in this place, that the head of stock was low in relation to area. Most farms already held enclosed land on the alluvium together with rough pasture in higher areas. Illegal intakes from the common under these circumstances may have held little appeal.

The pattern of the allotment boundaries which followed the apportionment of the common by the enclosure commissioners (Fig. 43) was as distinctive in Morfa Dyffryn as in Ceri. Almost all the boundary hedges or fences were intended to be straight but there was a great difference in size between the fields close to the already-enclosed land and those nearer the sea. The allotments in the east of the area covered most of the alluvial land which had not previously been enclosed. In both shape and size these fields were very comparable with those shown by the ten farm plans already mentioned to have been in use for meadow and pasture on the enclosed alluvium. In the west, and roughly co-extensive with the belt of sandhills, the commissioners created a small number of very large blocks of land. There can have been little local demand for these areas of unstable dunes, which are still unused agriculturally today, and it was directed that the four large enclosures to the south of the spit should be sold, presumably to defray the expenses of promoting and executing the act. The boundary between the old and new enclosures was not nearly as pronounced as in Ceri. The main contrasts which persist to the present-day map[1] are between the extensive but virtually unused dunes, the smaller symmetrical fields upon the alluvium, and the intricate network of tiny fields on the rocks of Cambrian age; distinctions which, despite differences in the dates of development, show strongly the influence of the physical setting.

The ownership pattern developed by the commissioners was a simple one; a fact to which the flat land and the uncomplicated common boundary were undoubtedly contributory. The large blocks of dune were sold and the smaller enclosures upon the alluvium were allocated as far as possible to the owners of adjacent land. These plots thus became, not only in shape and size but also in ownership,

[1] See 1 : 25,000 O.S. sheet SH,52.

physical extensions of the farms adjoining the common. Only one example exists in Fig. 43 of a field completely detached from the rest of the owner's holding. Owners whose land was not contiguous with the common inevitably were alloted land away from their farms. Many of the allotments not numbered in Fig. 43 became parts of fragmented holdings.

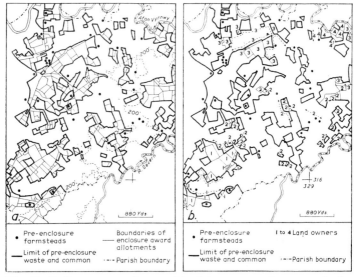

Fig. 44. Parliamentary enclosure of lowlying waste and common in the parishes of Llandrinio and Llandysilio, Montgomeryshire, 1799

a. Enclosure award allotments. No field boundaries are shown in the areas already enclosed.

b. The ownership pattern. The allotments to four selected owners are shown.

(Source: N.L.W., Montgomeryshire County Council Deposit, 19R.)

Coastal reclamation of another kind is illustrated by the enclosure of Traeth Mawr, the tidal sands of the estuary of Afon Glaslyn on the border of Caernarvonshire and Merioneth. Following an act of 1807[1] an embankment was built across the estuary which allowed the land behind it to be enclosed and improved. Though the pattern of the allotment boundaries shown in the award[2] was different from that on Morfa Dyffryn the nature of the land ownership was essentially the same.

[1] 47 Geo. III, c. 36.
[2] See J. I. Jones, 'An agricultural geography of the Glaslyn valley', unpublished thesis, M.Sc., University of Wales, 1957, map 10.

The lowlying marsh and valley land

The number of acts which authorized the enclosure of lowlying marsh and valley land were few in comparison with the two types already discussed, probably because not much other lowland of any kind remained unenclosed in Wales by the turn of the eighteenth century. The example reproduced here (Fig. 44) is an extract from an award dated 1799, following an act eleven years earlier,[1] and shows parts of the parishes of Llandrinio and Llandysilio, Montgomery-shire. The land lies between the rivers Severn and Vyrnwy, a few miles upstream of their confluence, and is nowhere more than a few feet above normal river level; indeed parts of the area are below, and the act provided for the embanking of the two streams.[2]

It is clear from Fig. 44 that, despite the difference in altitude and physical features generally, the pre-enclosure common in this area resembled that in the parish of Ceri more than the lowland, coastal common of Morfa Dyffryn. In the riverine parishes the boundary of the common was involved; small remnants of common lay isolated and completely surrounded by enclosed land and encroachment, both the intakes of farms abutting the common and enclosures completely within it, had taken place repeatedly. Two small en-croachments near the centre of the map and another in the south-west have all the qualities of squatter enclosure. All these characteristics imply that, as in Ceri, the land of the common was very desirable.

When the award allotments are considered there are few similari-ties between Fig. 44 and either of the awards previously illustrated. The fields were, on average, much smaller than those in Ceri or Morfa Dyffryn and, though boundaries were composed of straight lines, the allotments were more irregular in shape. It is almost impossible to distinguish between these fields and the adjacent fields in the longer-enclosed areas.[3] The sizes of fields created by the award were variable but, judging by the distribution, physical con-ditions were not casual, as at Morfa Dyffryn. The only exception is provided by the very smallest enclosures which were intended for buildings; like the pre-enclosure farmsteads these were all at or

[1] 28 Geo. III, c. 49.
[2] See discussion, M.C.J., 'The enclosure of common lands in Montgomeryshire, II', *Montgomeryshire Collections*, 15 (1882), 192–3.
[3] See 1 : 25,000 O.S. sheet SH,52.

above 200 feet, clear of the Severn and Vyrnwy flood-waters. Generally the differences in size seem to have been the result of the difficulties of apportioning such a complex common.

The ownership pattern resulting from the award (Fig. 44 b) reflects these same difficulties. Four typical landowners have been shown in the map and, of these, owner 4 in the north-east had the only compact holding, though even this was not fully consolidated as one small triangular field was detached from the rest of his property. Owners 1 and 3, who held larger pre-enclosure estates, received many allotments adjacent to their compact holdings, but clearly this was not always possible. Some allotted fields were detached from the rest, occasionally at some distance. The estate of owner 2 was already much fragmented and it is not surprising that his allotments were well dispersed. Again one of the effects of parliamentary enclosure was that holdings were unconsolidated.

The open arable fields

The open arable field is the last of the four types of land liable to be enclosed during the Napoleonic wars, and it is the only one for which there is little record of enclosure.[1] It is true that many awards, particularly those in Montgomeryshire, arranged for the exchange and re-allocation of arable strips, but the common fields with which they dealt were nearly always under pasture and meadow. Here then is a further contrast[2] between the areas where open arable fields still existed and the remaining areas in Wales. Not only were the open fields alien in origin, supporting farming methods and societies which were different, but they also resisted enclosure at a time when the movement to enclose was well underway elsewhere. The reason for this is not clear, but it may well be that because the open fields were situated generally in lowland areas of good arable land there was no immediate incentive, at a time when arable farming was more profitable than it had been for many years, to enclose and certainly not to change to a pastoral economy.

The result of parliamentary enclosure in Wales was that large parts of the agricultural area of the country were modified. The enclosure movement in Wales had a different emphasis from that in England. New hedges, fences, and access roads were created, as in England, but there were far fewer changes in farming practice.

[1] But see letter from T. I. J. Jones, *Agricultural History Review*, 8 (1960), 45.
[2] Supra, 129.

For example, the newly-enclosed upland moors were divided by a network of earth balks or dry stone walls but often stock was depastured on the rough grass in precisely the same way as it had been before enclosure, except that instead of being able to range freely the animals were contained within the large new fields. Little was done to improve the quality of the grass; indeed it was not until the present century that serious efforts were made to reclaim upland pasture. Probably the most noticeable feature of the examples studied above is that post-enclosure holdings were often fragmented. In some areas plots of land were sold or exchanged in order to produce compact holdings but in the uplands many of the large blocks of land, detached from the original properties, became self-contained hill farms. In these circumstances there was a tendency for the long-established link, in which the economies of both upland and lowland were under unified control, to break and for the system of transhumance, originally so widely practised, to disappear.[1] The hill farms now became suppliers of store cattle and sheep, supplementing their grassland in winter by feeding stuffs bought from the lowlands or abroad. It was the economic instability of these farms which led to the recent government-sponsored *Mid Wales investigation*.[2] It is difficult to think of examples of other processes, operating over a comparable length of time, which produced such marked changes and such lasting effects in the countryside as the statutory enclosure awards.

[1] But see also E. Davies, 'Sheep farming in upland Wales', *Geography*, 20 (1935), 97–111.
[2] Welsh Agricultural Land Sub-Commission, *Mid-Wales investigation report* (H.M.S.O., London, 1955).

IV. LITERARY EVIDENCE

CHAPTER 9

THE BOARD OF AGRICULTURE REPORTS, 1794–1796

So far the emphasis in this study has been upon differences in space. In a period such as the Napoleonic wars it is also necessary to study changes through time, and it is here that the literary evidence is of value. The earlier quarto reports of the Board of Agriculture refer to the period 1794–96 and the later octavo reports to the years 1810–14. Though it is difficult to compare literary and statistical material, when these reports are examined together with the Acreage Returns of 1801 three largely independent period pictures are available which allow a study of the progress of agricultural reform.[1]

The restricted scope of the 1801 returns, which dealt with the acreages of crops only, has meant that comparisons between the three periods 1794–96, 1801, and 1810–14 are limited to the cropped land and that attention must be focused largely upon changes in crop distributions and rotations. The introduction of a new crop, such as turnips, which had not previously been grown extensively, or the adoption of more rational cropping methods are the indices of change. In this respect the diffusion of the popular Norfolk four-course system is particularly interesting. Despite the intense economic pressure, its spread was controlled by accessibility to the areas in which the rotation was already established and by the ecological requirements of the crops. As previous chapters have shown, the growth of wheat, barley, and turnips was severely restricted in uplands areas and this, combined with the need for constant tillage, ensured that turnip husbandry was best adapted to easily worked, lowland soils.

The literary evidence is important for other reasons. The Board of Agriculture reports, particularly, contain information on aspects of agriculture not included in other sources. For example, they treat of the use of grassland and of the nature of farming systems,

---

[1] For a previous study of this type see D. Thomas, 'Agricultural changes in the Welsh Borderland: a cultural diffusion at the turn of the eighteenth century', *Transactions of the Honourable Society of Cymmrodorion* (1961), 101–14.

neither of which was covered by the statistical surveys and which can only be inferred from the cartographic material. The coverage of the literary evidence is also more comprehensive in area and information is available on the two counties, Anglesey and Caernarvon, for which no 1801 returns are extant. The existence of a number of surveys, having at least one subject in common, makes it possible to gauge the accuracy of each by comparing one with another, though in a period of change this approach is necessarily limited. But it is possible, for example, to see that Kay's *General view of the agriculture of north Wales* lacks thoroughness and that the section on Denbighshire is especially weak, being based more upon hearsay than accurate field observation.

In the following discussion of the quarto reports of the Board of Agriculture conditions in Wales in the years 1794–96 are considered within the framework of the major regional divisions shown in Fig. 29.

The Highland Regions

It is unfortunate that Kay's account of north Wales was poor because much of the Highland Regions lay in the counties upon which he reported. Over most of Caernarvonshire, which by analogy must have been very similar to the adjacent O regions in Denbighshire and Merioneth, the rotation practised was first year—oats, second—barley, and then oats repeatedly.[1] For Mynydd Hiraethog there is no information but in Merioneth, where the amount of cropland was small, oats were the principal grain with a little barley also grown. Potatoes were cultivated but turnips were seldom sown.[2] In the reports on Montgomeryshire and Cardiganshire oats and rye were mentioned as important crops.[3] Clark's description of Radnorshire referred specially to the mountainous hundred of Rhayader,[4] which was roughly co-extensive with the O–OR regions of Fig. 29.[5] Here the practice was to plough one of the drier plots of land which had been under pasture for some years, manure it as heavily as possible, reap a crop of barley in the first year and afterwards take successive crops of oats until the land did not return the seed. Rye

---

[1] G. Kay, *General view of . . . Caernarvonshire* (Edinburgh, 1794), 12.

[2] G. Kay, *General view of . . . Merionethshire* (Edinburgh, 1794), 12.

[3] G. Kay, *General view of . . . Montgomeryshire* (Edinburgh, 1794), 15–16; T. Lloyd and [D.] Turnor, *General view of . . . Cardigan* (London, 1794), 25–6.

[4] J. Clark, *General view of . . . Radnor* (London, 1794), 11–14.

[5] W. Rees, *An historical atlas of Wales* (Cardiff, 1951), plate 57.

was sometimes grown instead of barley after the initial ploughing.[1] In an appendix to the report two rotations were recommended to the landowners of the uplands areas.[2] On the best arable Clark suggested: first year—turnips, strongly manured, second—barley with clover, third—clover, fourth—wheat, fifth—oats, or better, fallow, to be used for continuous cropping, while on the poorer land: first year— oats, second—fallow, third—wheat, fourth—peas, fifth—oats, sixth—fallow, seventh—turnips, eighth—barley, to be followed by four or five years under clover or rye-grass. In the hilly parts of Brecknockshire oats were again the dominant grain, and sometimes as many as seven successive crops were taken off the same piece of land, though a little barley and rye were also grown.[3] In his Pembrokeshire and Carmarthenshire reports Hassall was concerned mainly with the southern parts of the counties and did not deal with the uplands to the north.

The reports by the Board of Agriculture surveyors upon the Highland Regions were, for the most part, lacking in detail, but when compared with the series of maps derived from the statistical enquiry of 1801 it is clear that there are few inconsistencies. Kay, it is true, did not mention potatoes in his description of Montgomery-shire, though in 1801 they ranked third in two parishes and occupied more than 5 per cent of the cropland in the western half of the county (Fig. 19), and Clark underestimated the importance of rye in Radnorshire where, seven years later, as much as 20 per cent of the cropland was devoted to it. These small differences are more likely to be the result of omissions on the parts of the authors of the written accounts than of changes in farming practice, for as such they would represent a regression in husbandry methods in a period of great agricultural advance. The picture in 1801, then, was much as it was in 1794. No evidence exists of any agricultural reform between the two dates, and Clark's suggested rotations do not seem to have been adopted with any enthusiasm by the farmers of upland Radnorshire. There is no trace of the ambitious system, including one more grain crop than the Norfolk four-course, which he recom-mended for the better parts of the uplands, and though WOBPe regions appear in lowland Radnorshire in Fig. 29 and are akin to

---

[1] J. Clark, op. cit., 18.
[2] Ibid., 36.
[3] J. Clark, *General view of . . . Brecknock* (London, 1794), 35.

his second suggestion, it will be shown later that this crop association already existed in 1794 and was not found on poor quality upland soils as Clark had intended.

Grassland occupied by far the greater part of the Highland Regions and, despite its poor quality, supported a large sheep population, but in north Wales particularly, black cattle were also raised in the uplands.[1] Almost all the authors of the Board of Agriculture surveys deplored the transhuming livestock system based upon the interdependence of enclosed farm and common moorland, though for different reasons. Kay reported that the upland commons were underpopulated but overstocked,[2] and Lloyd and Turnor complained about straying sheep.[3] Clark, in what was probably the most coherent attack, argued that the ease with which a living could be made from the common grazing encouraged idleness upon the enclosed farms and dishonesty upon the commons.[4] His contention that, because the defects of the system could not be corrected, enclosure was the only remedy, was echoed by the other authors.

The Peripheral Regions

In the OB regions to the west of the Highland Regions (Fig. 29) cropping in 1794–96 was less limited but hardly more enlightened. In Cardiganshire a large number of rotations were quoted but generally a crop of wheat was followed by two or three crops of barley and then the same number of oats before the land was returned to grass.[5] Sometimes one year in the rotation was devoted to peas and a few farmers cultivated turnips, though not in the Norfolk four-course. Potatoes were widely grown and, together with barley, they were one of the main food crops. In Carmarthenshire oats and barley were the dominant crops except in the extreme south of the county and in the wider valleys. Neither crops were of the highest quality but oats were produced in sufficient quantities to provide an export trade to Bristol and other places. Fallowing, more widespread in the south of the county than in the north, was usually associated with the rotation: first year—fallow, second—wheat, third—barley, fourth—peas, barley, or oats, and then oats continuously. A few more-enlightened farmers used the rotation:

---

[1] E.g. G. Kay (Montgomeryshire), op. cit., 18–20.
[2] G. Kay (Caernarvonshire), op. cit., 16–17.
[3] T. Lloyd and [D,] Turnor, op. cit., 22–3.
[4] J. Clark (Brecknock), op. cit., 34, 39–43.
[5] T. Lloyd and [D.] Turnor, op. cit., 10–11, 25–8.

first year—fallow, second—wheat, third—barley, fourth—oats, fifth—clover and rye-grass.[1] In the Pembrokeshire report Hassall did not assign the rotations quoted to any particular area, but two of the three were dominated by oats and barley, with peas and wheat occurring much less frequently.[2] For coastal Merioneth and Llŷn there are no details, but Anglesey, for which there were no 1801 returns but where cropping must have been very like that in the OB region to the south, is well documented.[3] The usual method was to plant either oats or barley continuously, but sometimes alternately, for a number of years until the land was exhausted and then to sow clover or rye-grass seeds. Two rotations had recently been introduced: first year—fallow, second—barley with clover or rye-grass, third—hay, fourth—oats, fifth—turnips, and first year—fallow, second—wheat, third—hay, fourth—turnips, fifth—barley with grass seeds. But it is clear from Kay's statement that only a few fields of turnips were to be found in the county that these rotations could not have been widely used. Unlike Cardiganshire, the quantity of potatoes grown in Anglesey was insufficient to meet the needs of the county and there were frequent imports from Ireland, mainly through the port of Amlwch on the north coast.

In the remaining Peripheral Regions (WO, WOB, and WOBPe in Fig. 29) wheat was of greater importance during the years 1794–96 but farming methods were little more advanced. In Flintshire fifty years before Kay's report, rye had been grown more extensively than either wheat or barley, and oats were planted continuously in the same ground.[4] In 1794 the chief crops were wheat and oats with barley, beans, peas, potatoes, and clover grown in smaller quantities but, as in the OB region, green crops were rarely integrated in the rotations. Where fallowing was practised a typical rotation was: first year—fallow, second—wheat, third—barley, fourth—oats, continuously, but a few farmers used: first year—oats, second—potatoes, third—wheat, fourth—barley with grass seed. In the 'fertile vales' of Montgomeryshire practices varied but the most popular seems to have been that in which a hay crop was followed by wheat, and then barley, oats, or peas. Where turnips were culti-vated they were generally sown after grass or oats and were invariably

[1] C. Hassall, *General view of . . . Carmarthen* (London, 1794), 13–14.
[2] C. Hassall, *General view of . . . Pembroke* (London, 1794), 16–17.
[3] G. Kay, *General View of . . . Anglesey* (Edinburgh, 1794), 12–15.
[4] G. Kay, *General view of . . . Flintshire* (Edinburgh, 1794), 10–15.

followed by barley and grass seeds.[1] For Denbighshire there is no detailed information but Clark was quite specific about the lower parts of Radnorshire, for which he quoted two rotations.[2] The first (first year—wheat, second—peas, third—barley and clover, fourth— clover, fifth—clover, sixth—fallow) was the practice of the good farmer; the less enlightened used a rotation including oats (first year—wheat, second—barley, third—peas, fourth—oats with clover, fifth—clover, sixth—fallow). In the Brecknockshire report Clark described five rotations in use in the lowland hundred of Talgarth.[3] Of these, three contained wheat, oats, barley, and peas in equal proportions while the fourth, the rotation of good farmers, included wheat, barley, peas, and clover leys. On coarse neglected soils wheat, oats, and barley were the main crops. In the Vale of Usk a nine-course rotation was practised including wheat, oats, barley, peas, and turnips. The report on Monmouthshire is far less precise. Wheat, oats, and barley were the principal crops with peas important in the east and beans upon the heavier soils. Two rotations containing turnips were mentioned, but not located.[4] In the survey of Glamorgan information is scant outside the Vale but further west in Carmarthenshire it is possible to distinguish descriptions of areas which fall within the WOB region.[5] In the wider valleys and in the area around Laugharne wheat was of greater importance than elsewhere in the county. Upon Laugharne Marsh a distinctive rotation was in use: first year—wheat, second—beans, third barley. In Pembrokeshire, where wheat, oats, and barley were the main crops, turnips had been introduced a few years before the date of the report.[6]

The statistics of 1801 again reflect the conditions described by the Board of Agriculture surveyors. The OB region (Fig. 29) is completely consistent with the reports for Cardiganshire, north Carmarthenshire, and north Pembrokeshire; indeed the comparison of the two sources bears closer examination. For example, in Cardiganshire, where potatoes and peas were of importance in 1794, Figs. 19 and 20 show that in 1801 the crops occupied more than 5 per cent of the cropland over considerable areas and in many parishes

[1] G. Kay (Montgomeryshire), op. cit., 15–16.
[2] J. Clark (Radnor), op. cit., 18.
[3] J. Clark (Brecknock), op. cit., 19–22.
[4] J. Fox, General view of . . . Monmouth (Brentford, 1794), 13–14.
[5] C. Hassall (Carmarthen), op. cit., 13–15.
[6] C. Hassall (Pembroke), op. cit., 16–17.

ranked third above wheat (cf. Figs. 26 and 27). In the eastern and south coast Peripheral Regions the same correspondence is evident. In Flintshire and Montgomeryshire the WOB region (Fig. 29) is consistent with Kay's accounts and there is also sufficient evidence of the other crops which he reported to lend credence to his statements. Potatoes, peas, and beans are all shown by the 1801 maps to have been grown in Flintshire (Figs. 19–21) but, of course, Kay was unable to distinguish the differences in distribution which the maps indicate, just as he failed to note the differences in the standing of wheat, oats, and barley shown by the 1801 crop rank analysis (Figs. 24–6). Evidence of Kay's turnip—barley association exists in south-east Montgomeryshire, where in a few parishes turnips occupied over 5 per cent of the cropland, and in three ranked fourth with barley in a higher position. Clark's descriptions of Radnorshire and Brecknockshire are again supported by the 1801 returns. Here, the absence of a WBPe region, the fact that in only four parishes in the two counties did peas rank higher than oats, and the widespread occurrence of WOBPe regions (Fig. 29) suggests that the majority of farmers were still what Clark considered to be unenlightened. The nine-course rotation in the Vale of Usk is clearly reflected in the 1801 figures where several parishes returned wheat, oats, barley, peas, and turnips in the first five places. One parish, Llangattock nigh Usk, in the Monmouthshire section of the valley, had a WOBPeT crop index. Most of the other 1801 returns for Monmouthshire tally with Fox's account, and the area where turnips were of importance can be distinguished in the south-east; in one parish they occupied over 20 per cent of the cropland (Fig. 22). In lowland Carmarthenshire and Pembrokeshire the WOB region accords with the earlier descriptions and the standing of turnips and beans (Fig. 27) reflects some of Hassall's more detailed remarks.

The authors of the Board of Agriculture reports were no more enthusiastic about the management of grassland than they were about the cropland. In no part of the Peripheral Regions had the short clover or rye-grass ley, so popular in south-eastern England, been widely adopted. In Anglesey Kay complained that fields were left too long under grass,[1] and in Flintshire he reported that artificial

---

[1] G. Kay (Anglesey), op. cit., 17.

grassland was unpopular because it was inferior to the longer-established pastures, the land always being exhausted before grass seeds were sown.[1] The account of Radnorshire by Clark confirms the impression gained from all the crop rotations quoted for the Peripheral Regions, that clover and grass seed was sown only when arable land was being restored to permanent pasture. In the west the grassland was employed mainly for the production of livestock. The dominant breed of cattle was the black variety which was able to withstand winters in the open upon poor fodder. These were sold to drovers, who herded them to the markets of the lowlands to the east. From Anglesey, for example, 10,000 head of cattle, about one-quarter of the total number on the island, were exported annually, swimming across the Menai Strait near Bangor. Two drovers accounted for nearly half this export. Sheep, also reared in large numbers, often reached the markets in the same way.[2]

In the eastern and southern Peripheral Regions grassland supported a more varied economy. Breeds of cattle and sheep differed from county to county. For example, in upland Montgomeryshire[3] black cattle were reared, but in the lowlands, as in Flintshire,[4] the native breed was crossed with English bulls. To the south in lowland Radnorshire the borderland breeds of Shropshire and Herefordshire had replaced the native cattle,[5] but in Brecknockshire attempts to introduce breeds from the east had not been a success.[6] In south Monmouthshire[7] and Glamorgan[8] the native breed was still widespread, but these were not the black cattle of other parts of Wales; the Glamorgan breed was usually small and dark brown in colour. Further west in Carmarthenshire[9] and Pembrokeshire[10] black cattle were again the most prominent variety but of better quality than in mid and north Wales. The end-products of the stock economy in the eastern and southern Peripheral Regions also varied from place to place. In some areas livestock was sold to the drovers very much

---

[1] G. Kay (Flintshire), op. cit., 16.
[2] G. Kay (Anglesey), op. cit., 24–6.
[3] G. Kay (Montgomeryshire), op. cit., 20.
[4] G. Kay (Flintshire), op. cit., 20–1.
[5] J. Clark (Radnor), op. cit., 18–19.
[6] J. Clark (Brecknock), op. cit., 15.
[7] J. Fox (Monmouth), op. cit., 14–15.
[8] J. Fox, *General view of . . . Glamorgan* (London, 1796), 22.
[9] C. Hassall (Carmarthen), op. cit., 35.
[10] C. Hassall (Pembroke), op. cit., 45.

as in the west, for example in Montgomeryshire[1] and Monmouthshire,[2] but in the south-west dairying was important.[3] From Pembrokeshire salt butter in casks and earthenware pots, and cheeses were exported to London, Bristol, and other centres.

The general impression of the Peripheral Regions gained from the accounts of the Board of Agriculture surveyors, and from their comparison with the Acreage Returns of 1801, is well summarized by Hassall in his report on Carmarthenshire and Pembrokeshire.[4] Apart from the gentlemen farmers there seemed throughout the country a general prejudice against anything which was new or different from the traditional methods. While all farmers acknowledged the advantages of improved systems, few practised them. Some offered the excuse that to adopt English fashions would make them the butts of their neighbours, and others, with some justification,[5] defended their methods with the argument that to restore their land to pasture in good heart would prompt their landlords to raise rents when farm leases expired. To excite the spirit of improvement in such circumstances was a very difficult task.

The Ingressive Regions

There is no precise information in the Board of Agriculture report for Denbighshire about the WB region in the Vale of Clwyd. However, Kay makes it clear that though soils in many parts of the county were suited to turnips and other green crops, these were seldom cultivated. A few farmers, it is true, used the rotation: first year—turnips, second—barley, third—clover and rye-grass, fourth—wheat, for continuous cropping by dividing their arable as nearly as possible into four and every year sowing one of the crops in each quarter, but they were exceptional.[6] In Monmouthshire it has already been suggested that the two rotations, quoted by Fox, which contained turnips (first year—turnips, second—peas, third—wheat, fourth—barley, fifth—clover, and first year—wheat, second—turnips, third—barley, fourth—clover) were used in the south-east of the county but there is nothing to indicate how extensively they were employed.[7] It is quite possible that, as in Denbighshire, they

---

[1] G. Kay (Montgomeryshire), op. cit., 20.
[2] J. Fox (Monmouth), op. cit., 14.
[3] C. Hassall (Carmarthen), op. cit., 37–8; idem. (Pembroke), op. cit., 40–1.
[4] E.g. C. Hassall (Pembroke), op. cit., 37.
[5] See D. Williams, *The Rebecca riots* (Cardiff, 1955), 65–6.
[6] G. Kay, *General view of . . . Denbighshire* (Edinburgh, 1794), 14–15.
[7] J. Fox (Monmouth), op. cit., 13–14.

represent the practices of the gentlemen farmers only. Fox writes enthusiastically and at length on the Vale of Glamorgan which he describes as 'the garden of south Wales, as the Vale of Clwyd is reckoned to be that of north Wales'.[1] Wheat, oats, and barley were the major grain crops, and peas, beans, and vetches were alternated with them but the rotations are not given. Turnips seem to have been little known judging by the hints, included in the report, for sowing and using the crop.[2] An appendix to Kay's account reproduces one set of answers to a questionnaire circulated by the Board of Agriculture. The replies were meant to be incorporated in the report, but that of John Franklin arrived too late and was printed in full. The details obviously refer to Judge John Franklin of Llanmihangel Place, a few miles south of Cowbridge, who, as Lewis confirms,[3] lived there for sixty years. He was clearly a progressive landowner and though his statements cannot be regarded as typical they do reflect the work and attitudes of the limited number of improvers in the Vale of Glamorgan. Wheat, oats, and barley were again the main crops mentioned, but peas, beans, and turnips had been introduced not long before the replies to the questions were written and were alternated with the grain crops. The stimulus to progress came partly from the financial rewards of more efficient farming but also, paradoxically when the arguments of Hassall are remembered, from the prestige to be gained among those with a bent for reform. The spirit of improvement was obviously alive in this area.

The tenuous evidence of the beginnings of agricultural reform in the Ingressive Regions in 1794–96 is supported by the Acreage Returns of 1801. In the WB region of the Vale of Clwyd not only were wheat and barley the typical crops but turnips occupied over 5 per cent of the cropland (Fig. 22); in one parish they ranked third after the two grains, and in two other parishes fourth (Figs. 26–7). This suggests that the new ideas had made progress since the date of Kay's report. There is stronger evidence of advances in cropping techniques in south-east Monmouthshire. Here, four parishes had a crop combination index of WBT (Fig. 28), and in those which were classified WB turnips often held third or fourth place (Figs. 26–7). In the Vale of Glamorgan, in only one parish were turnips sufficiently

---

[1] J. Fox (Glamorgan), op. cit., 15.

[2] Ibid., 25, 28.

[3] S. Lewis, *A topographical dictionary of Wales* (London, 1848), II, *sub nom.* Llanmihangel, 81.

popular to result in a WBT index. Though many of the WB parishes had turnips in third place, the distribution, like that of peas and beans, the other crops mentioned by Franklin, was uneven (Figs. 20–2). It is clear that the new turnip rotations had not been as widely adopted as in the Vale of Clwyd and south-east Monmouthshire, but the decline in the importance of oats signifies that changes had begun (Fig. 15).

Outside the Vale of Glamorgan there is no information on the extent, product, or management of grassland in the Ingressive Regions in 1794–96. In the Vale of Glamorgan Fox thought that too much of the land was in pasture.[1] A better balance between arable and pasture might have removed the need for grain imports, but, on the other hand, the popularity of Glamorgan livestock in the markets at least made the bias seem reasonable. Both sheep and cattle were reared, but mainly, it seems, upon permanent pasture. Clover, trefoil, rye-grass, and sainfoin were cultivated, for example, on the Franklin estate, but they were not grown extensively.

From the comparisons which have been made between the quarto reports of the Board of Agriculture and the Acreage Returns two important points have emerged which concern the accuracy of the written surveys. First, though the quarto reports were wide in scope it is clear when details of cropping are set against the 1801 figures that important facts were often omitted. For example, in the otherwise very good account of Radnorshire by Clark the OR region revealed in Fig. 29 was not mentioned; Kay failed to note the distinctive cropping practices of the north Merioneth littoral shown in the rank order maps, and Fox paid scant attention to the Caldicot Level, the only place in Wales where beans occupied over 20 per cent of the cropland (Fig. 21). Secondly, there is wide variation in the quality of the work of the different Board of Agriculture authors. Clark of Builth, Brecknockshire, the land agent and steward to Lord Hereford, produced accounts for Radnorshire and Brecknockshire which were both detailed and discerning. With the one exception already noted, there is little that can be added to his reports from other sources. Kay, on the other hand, is guilty of many omissions. He failed, for example, to distinguish the differences in the importance of the various grain crops between coastal and inland Flintshire, and particularly noticeable is his neglect of the Vale of

[1] J. Fox (Glamorgan), op. cit., 15, 20–1.

Clwyd. The reasons for Kay's lack of detail are not hard to find. He was a substitute for the original surveyor and began his investigation later than most other authors; yet he managed to survey six counties, more than any other author, and prepare his report for publication in 1794. He was also unable to speak Welsh. Even with the aid of the interpreters, whose help he acknowledges,[1] the task of gaining anything more than a superficial impression of the general level of farming in such counties as Caernarvon and Merioneth must have been almost impossible.

[1] See introductory letter, *General view of . . . north Wales* (Edinburgh, 1794).

CHAPTER 10

THE BOARD OF AGRICULTURE REPORTS, 1810–1814

THE octavo reports of the Board of Agriculture are more uniform in content and quality than the quarto reports. The account of Monmouthshire was written by Hassall, but all the remaining counties of Wales were surveyed by one man, Walter Davies, though in south Wales he was greatly assisted by Edward Williams (Iolo Morganwg), who accompanied him on his travels, and by the evidence of landowners and of the clergy. The task which Davies undertook was an immense one, but as a scholar and a man with considerable local knowledge—he was Rector of Manafon, Montgomeryshire—he contrived to avoid the superficiality characteristic of the work of Kay. The corollary of this is that Davies's survey was more extended in time than those of any of the earlier authors. The reports of 1794–96 rest upon very fresh investigations; the Board of Agriculture, which commissioned the authors, was not itself founded until August 1793, and so most of the surveys must have been completed within a year, and the Glamorgan survey within three years. Davies's work spans fifteen years or more. There is evidence that his account of north Wales was begun before the turn of the century though it was not first published until 1810.[1] Fortunately for this study in which the chronology of crop-rotation improvement is a major aim, there is every reason to suppose that the sections on cropping were compiled later, between 1804 and 1808.[2] The parts of the south Wales report that deal with cropping seem to have been derived from a survey carried out between 1810 and 1812.[3] Hassall's account of Monmouthshire, the only octavo report of which he was author, was written in 1810 and 1811.[4]

The Highland Regions

Davies first mentions the Highland Regions (Fig. 29) under the heading of 'Rotations of a better kind' when he describes cropping in a 'Snowdonian climate, about one-third as high as the peak';

[1] W. Davies, *General view of . . . north Wales* (London, 1810), 203, 252.
[2] E.g. ibid., 177, 189–91.
[3] W. Davies, *General view of . . . south Wales* (London, 1814), I, 282, 299, 339, 389–90.
[4] C. Hassall, *General view of . . . Monmouth* (London, 1812), 10, 44, 68.

that is, at around 1,000 feet.[1] Here the rotation practised was: first year—oats, second—barley, third—turnips or potatoes, fourth—barley, with grass seed for pasture. There is no indication of how extensive was this method in Caernarvonshire but his reports of other parts of the Highland Regions suggest that better rotations were being adopted very slowly. In Dyffryn Edeirnion, north-east Merioneth, upon loamy gravels, Davies described the rotation: first year—oats, second—wheat, third—barley, fourth—peas, fifth—wheat, sixth—barley with grass seeds;[2] but elsewhere in the county cropping was unenlightened. A number of attempts had been made to introduce turnips. At first, despite the success of trials on the larger estates, turnip culture did not spread rapidly through the county, but after the turn of the century the attitude of farmers gradually began to change under the stimulus of premiums offered by agricultural societies for improved working, and Davies had every hope that the crop would quickly become widespread.[3] Meanwhile oats were still harvested by the most primitive methods in the higher areas.[4] In upland Montgomeryshire similar cropping practices prevailed. Oats were grown on newly ploughed land for as many as five years in succession before the land was restored to pasture; when barley was cultivated it was confined to south-facing slopes. Two rotations appear to be those used in the uplands. These were dominated by oats but both had wheat as the second course and it is noticeable that neither contained a green crop.[5] Upon the recently enclosed upland moors the land was sometimes pared, burnt, and then sown with rye, which usually produced a good crop. The better farmers followed rye with oats, repeating the sequence where conditions permitted, and then finally sowing grass seeds, but others allowed the land to revert naturally to a poor pasture after the first crop of rye.[6] In contrast in north-west Radnorshire, where Davies reported that improved methods had recently been introduced, the general rotation was: first year—turnips, second—barley with clover, third—clover, fourth—wheat, fifth—oats; the land was then either returned to grass for two or three years or the rotation was begun again. On the better arable land a twelve-course rotation was used in which wheat occurred three times and barley four, but it also included four non-grain crops: turnips, peas, and clover

[1] W. Davies (1810), op. cit., 154.   [4] Ibid., 167.
[2] Ibid., 159.   [5] Ibid., 161–4.
[3] Ibid., 202–3.   [6] Ibid., 193–4.

(twice).[1] From the higher ground near Trecastell, Brecknockshire, the following rotations were reported: first year—wheat, second—barley, third—peas, fourth—oats with clover, and first year—wheat, second—barley, third—oats with clover, while to the south of Brecon and in the Honddu valley in the Black Mountains similar methods were used.[2] In one part of upland Carmarthenshire overlooking the Vale of Tywi barley was the most important crop (first year—wheat, second—barley, third—oats, fourth—barley with clover and grass seed)[3] but generally throughout the highlands of Cardiganshire, Carmarthenshire, and Pembrokeshire oats remained the favourite grain and provided the main export.[4]

A comparison between the octavo reports on the Highland Regions and the earlier material suggests that though improvements had been made the progress was recent and incomplete. Between 1794–96 and 1801 there had been no change in cropping methods but shortly after 1801 it is clear that more rational rotations were spreading, particularly into the east of the area. In the counties to the west of the moorland core the higher areas were still concerned mainly with the production of oats; it was in a few places only, such as in north-east Merioneth where access to the east was easy, that changes had occurred. The counties to the east were more susceptible to change. In Brecknockshire and Radnorshire wheat seems to have gained in importance in the upland areas. In 1801 the crop had generally ranked third, with oats and either barley or rye more important (Figs. 24–6), and had sometimes occupied less than 5 per cent of the cropland (Fig. 12). Davies's report suggests that within ten years wheat had achieved a standing equal to that of oats and barley in some places. In upland Radnorshire it is interesting to note that the very rotation which Clark had suggested in 1794, and of which no trace could be detected in 1801, was now in use, though modified by the introduction of short leys. The farmers of Montgomeryshire seem to have been less progressive but wheat did appear in two of the reported rotations and, of course, the survey of that county was earlier by a few years. The progress made in the eastern Highland Regions in the decade after 1801 is shown by the increasing diversification of the cropping; wheat gained in importance, short leys were introduced, and non-grain crops began to appear in rotations, though turnips made little

[1] W. Davies (1814), I), op. cit., 367–8, 512.
[2] Ibid., 311–14.
[3] Ibid., 314–15.
[4] Ibid., 476–7.

headway outside Radnorshire. But these improvements should not be overemphasized. The general state of cropping in the uplands must still have been, to use Davies's own words, 'repugnant to the theories of the agriculturists of more happy climates'.

As one might expect, there is no evidence that these first scattered improvements in arable working caused any changes in the use made of grassland, though it is probable that the proportion of land under grass fell as the war continued. Davies was as critical as the earlier authors of the length of time that land was left in pasture and also of the methods used to return land to grass after an arable course. In upland Caernarvonshire, Denbighshire, and Merioneth, for example, farmers who did not allow their grassland to regenerate naturally imported hay-seeds from Anglesey; seeds in which a high proportion was of the ribwort.[1] By whichever method pasture was established the results could not have been very satisfactory. The sheep, and particularly in north Wales the cattle, which this land supported were not of the highest quality. They were smaller than similar breeds in the adjacent lowlands, mainly a result of the lack of attention and planned breeding.[2] The authors of the quarto reports had all recommended enclosure of the upland wastes, but fifteen years later, when the results of many awards were evident, it is clear that the enclosure movement in Wales also had its opponents among informed agriculturalists, and that it had not proved the panacea of the ills of the uplands.[3]

The Peripheral Regions

The OB region of west Wales shown in Fig. 29 underwent changes after 1801 very similar to those of the eastern Highland Regions. While generally there was little attempt at improvement, better rotations were reported from a number of isolated places. Near the town of Cardigan and from two parts of the plateau-land of the north of the county Davies reported three-year rotations in which wheat was followed by barley and oats, and then pasture re-established by sowing clover or grass seed. In the valley of the Teifi turnips appeared in one rotation but generally the three-grain course was preferred. Occasionally peas were introduced into these

[1] W. Davies (1810), op. cit., 218.
[2] Ibid., 225, 312, 324; idem., *General view of . . . south Wales* (London, 1814), II. 243.
[3] W. Davies (1810), op. cit., 274–5; idem. (1814, II), op. cit., 109–13.

systems.[1] In Caernarvonshire a seven-course rotation (first year—oats, second—turnips or potatoes, third—barley with clover and rye-grass, fourth—hay, fifth—wheat, sixth—a green crop, seventh—barley with clover, and then pasture for a number of years) was reported but not located; a second rotation was attributed to the coastal parishes in the extreme north-east of the county (first year—wheat, second—barley, third—peas, fourth—wheat, fifth—wheat). In Llŷn and along the coasts to the north and east, better farmers used the Norfolk four-course and the same rotation appeared near Menai and in a few places elsewhere in Anglesey. One of the better rotations in Anglesey (first year—barley, second—clover and grasses, third—wheat, or on light land barley, fourth—turnips, fifth—barley with grass seed, then pasture for five or six years) shows evidence of local modification; though grain crops were not grown successively, barley, the bread corn, still dominated.[2] But these were not the practices of the bulk farmers. For Carmarthenshire six rotations were reported in the OB region and these show that oats and barley were the major crops. A typical rotation was: first year—wheat, second—barley, third—oats, fourth—barley, fifth—oats, and frequently sixth—oats. Sometimes clover or peas replaced one of the grain crops.[3] In Cardiganshire oats and barley were cropped continuously[4] and in north-west Merioneth the standard of farming was equally backward.[5] For Anglesey and Caernarvonshire Davies quotes two five-year rotations, both of which included only oats and barley. These, and not the improved rotations already mentioned, must have been the general systems because in Anglesey the proportion of wheat to oats was 1 : 22, and wheat to barley 1 : 14. Only in the cultivation of potatoes did the two north-western counties satisfy Davies.[6]

At the date of the octavo-report surveys agriculture in the Peripheral Regions to the east and south (Fig. 29, WO, WOB, WOBPe) was more modified by influences from the east. In Denbighshire and Flintshire the Norfolk rotation had been used on one farm for eighteen years, and more generally throughout the two counties long enough to have given rise to the opinion that in its pure form

[1] W. Davies (1814, I), op. cit., 318–19, 342, 350.
[2] W. Davies (1810), op. cit., 152–3.
[3] W. Davies (1814, I), op. cit., 315–18.
[4] Ibid., 319.
[5] W. Davies (1810), op. cit., 207.
[6] Ibid., 151–2, 207.

it was unsuited to the area. Some farmers therefore introduced peas into the system. But these were not the only cropping methods. On the Coal Measures soils in the district around Flint at least four different rotations were used, all containing wheat, barley, and oats. In two of the rotations the grain crops were grown in succession but in the other two potatoes, beans, and clover introduced diversity. Cropping practices were also varied in the lowlands of eastern Denbighshire. Together with the Norfolk four-course a rotation was reported in which wheat, oats, and peas appeared. On heavy soils the rotation: first year—turnips, second—wheat, third—oats with grass seeds, fourth—hay, fifth—pasture, sixth—wheat, was used and upon light land the following: first year—turnips, second—barley, third—maslin (wheat and rye mixed), fourth—turnips, fifth—barley with grass seeds. Where light land had been over-tilled turnips were followed by barley and then grassland.[1] In Montgomeryshire Davies records variants of the Norfolk rotation on the lighter soils; on the heavier land a number of rotations were employed in which wheat and barley were the main grains, but in which oats also appeared. In contrast with Anglesey, the proportion of wheat to barley in the vales was 4 : 3; an index of the difference still remaining between east and west. Turnips were sometimes grown to separate two grain crops, but more often peas were used for this purpose.[2]

Along the Radnorshire–Herefordshire border fields of turnips were a common sight, but in the valleys leading to the west the crop did not always occur frequently in rotations. To the north of Radnor Forest wheat, oats, barley, and peas were the main crops; in the broader Vale of Wye wheat, turnips, barley, and clover were often reported, though even here peas remained an important element.[3] For the Brecknockshire section of the Usk valley a large number of rotations were quoted. Some were modifications of the Norfolk system but in many of the others peas and oats occurred as frequently as wheat, barley, turnips, and clover.[4] The Peripheral Regions of Monmouthshire were more like the border country of Radnorshire. Of the seven rotations attributed to the Vale of Usk, most contained turnips, those on the heavier land included oats, but in none was peas grown. Indeed, it is noticeable that outside the Ingressive Regions in the south-east peas and beans were never

[1] Ibid., 154–9.
[2] Ibid., 160–2, 170.
[3] W. Davies (1814, I), op. cit., 310, 332–4, 512.
[4] Ibid., 310–13, 336, 365.

mentioned. Turnip culture, though not always practised in the classical manner, was well spread through the county and was established even in the mountainous hundred of Abergavenny, where the common rotation was: first year—wheat, second—barley, third—clover, fourth—wheat, fifth—turnips, sixth—barley, seventh —clover, eighth—wheat. Of the eighteen rotations which Hassall described in the county, three were the Norfolk four-course, while eight others included turnips, often as frequently as any other crop.[1] In contrast with the quarto report Davies quoted more than twenty different rotations for the Peripheral Regions of Glamorgan, but despite the large number they were remarkably consistent. Apart from the three main grains, wheat, oats, and barley, few other crops were grown. There were two reports of turnips from the coalfield and one of peas from the centre of the county, potatoes were grown on limestone soils in Gower and near Merthyr Tudful, but otherwise arable working was diversified only by the use of clover, which was employed both as a ley between two grain crops and also to produce a more permanent sward.[2] In the vales of Carmarthenshire the three grains also dominated, but here peas were more important and clover leys less frequent than in Glamorgan. Upon Laugharne Marsh beans were introduced into the grain rotation.[3] In south Pembrokeshire wheat, oats, barley, peas, and sometimes clover were used in rotations, wheat and barley occurring most frequently.[4]

A comparison with the statistics of 1801 shows how extensive were the changes which were taking place in the Peripheral Regions. In the OB region of west Wales (Fig. 29) progress was very slow. In Cardiganshire, north-west Merioneth, and north Pembrokeshire, the most inaccessible parts of the region which Davies described as 'the barley tract',[5] wheat seems to have gained in importance, though only in those areas where it was already third crop in 1801 (Fig. 26), but there is no evidence of the introduction of clover leys. To the north in Anglesey and Caernarvonshire easier communication with the east along the north Wales coast plain encouraged the spread of improved rotations containing turnips and one-year leys into the coastal lowlands. The Norfolk four-course and modified versions of it, occurred frequently but, though these rotations represent an

[1] C. Hassall, op. cit., 38–43, 47–8.
[2] W. Davies (1814, I), op. cit., 320–3, 328–30, 340–1, 349–50, 366, 371.
[3] Ibid., 315–16, 318, 337–8.
[4] Ibid., 330–2, 342.
[5] Ibid., 351.

active reform movement, they were not sufficiently widespread to alter the general character of the agriculture, which was much as it had been in 1794. In the remaining Peripheral Regions greater progress had been made. Upon the heavier soils of Denbighshire and Flintshire there had obviously been little change since 1801 when the WO and WOB regions were consistent with Davies's account, but on the lighter land he gives the impression that turnip husbandry was well established. As turnips rarely exceeded 5 per cent of the cropland or ranked as high as fourth crop outside the Vale of Clwyd in 1801 (Figs. 22, 27), extensive use of the crop must have been a recent innovation. The description of Montgomeryshire, on the other hand, coincides with the statistical survey, which showed wheat, oats, and barley to be the typical crops of the lowland parts of the county and, except in the south-east, peas to have been more important than turnips (Figs. 27, 29). The WOB and WOBPe regions of Brecknockshire and Radnorshire are also closely reflected in Davies's accounts and it is clear that, except in eastern Radnorshire, peas continued to be the most important non-grain crop. While there seem to have been few changes in the middle borderland between 1801 and the date of the octavo reports, in Monmouthshire turnip husbandry gained ground. In 1801 peas almost everywhere ranked higher than turnips and often occupied over 5 per cent of the cropland (Figs. 20, 27), but within ten years the crop had been displaced by turnips in almost all rotations. In the Peripheral Regions of the south Wales littoral to the west, no comparable transformation had occurred since 1801. It is possible that the clover leys, widely used in Glamorgan and also, though less often, in Carmarthenshire and Pembrokeshire, were recent introductions and that more wheat was being grown in south Pembrokeshire, but otherwise agriculture was broadly the same as in 1794–96.

Davies attempted to summarize the progress of cropping reform in south Wales by distinguishing three classes of rotation.[1] The first was the aristocratic or new system, practised mainly by the larger landowners, in which grain crops were alternated with green crops. The Norfolk rotation was the most popular course but modifications of it were also widely used. Increasingly landlords were persuading their tenants to adopt similar methods and some, for example, J. H. Lloyd of Cilybebyll, near Neath, Glamorgan, went further by

[1] Ibid., 306–7.

inserting clauses in renewed leases restraining tenants from growing more than three corn crops in succession.[1] The second class of rotation was the democratic or old system, presumably that of the small-holders and tenants, in which three or four grain crops were grown in succession and the land restored to grassland for as many years as it was under crops. The third class of miscellaneous rotations included those in which crops such as potatoes, beans, or buck-wheat occurred. In a consideration of the merits of the new and old systems Davies reprinted, with his own comments, the opinions of a correspondent not wholly in favour of the new system.[2] The conclusion to the discussion is that though the new system was sound, it was best adapted to sandy or chalky soils in areas of low rainfall. In much of Wales these conditions did not exist and therefore a compromise was necessary between the better aspects of the old system and the new. The most obvious modification needed in the new system was the introduction of the long ley; a change which, as the discussion above has shown, had already been widely adopted to meet local edaphic and climatic conditions.

The new methods of grassland management could not, in a short time, effect profoundly the standard or the nature of animal husbandry. Though improvements to grassland were not as limited in their spread by physical features as the new rotations with which they had been introduced, they had not been universally adopted by the date of the octavo reports. Apart from the general inertia of farmers, two factors hindered a wider extention. In some districts clover crops had failed repeatedly, and generally there was a belief that permanent grassland, though providing a smaller yield, was of better quality, producing superior milk, butter, and cheese, and fattening cattle more quickly.[3] The octavo reports thus do no more than sketch in some of the details of the livestock systems described by the earlier authors.

The Ingressive Regions

The material in the works of Davies and Hassall relating to the Ingressive Regions is much more detailed than that for the period 1794–96. In the Vale of Clwyd two general rotations were quoted: first year—peas or oats, second—wheat, third—turnips, fourth—barley, fifth—clover, sixth—wheat, seventh—barley, eighth—turnips,

[1] Ibid., 373.   [3] W. Davies (1810), op. cit., 212, 216.
[2] Ibid., 377–83.

and first year—turnips, second—barley, third—clover, fourth—wheat, fifth—peas, sixth—wheat, seventh—barley. Near St. Asaph upon thin soil which, when left untended, was colonized by dwarf furze and brambles, the rotation was: first year—wheat, second—peas, third—wheat, fourth—barley with grass and clover seeds. At the northern end of the Vale near Prestatyn beans and vetches (bean-like legumes) appeared in the rotations.[1] In the eastern part of the hundred of Caldicot, south-east Monmouthshire, turnips were even more important than elsewhere in the county. Excluding the three rotations which clearly refer to the Caldicot Level the tilled land was managed by use of the Norfolk four-course together with a rotation which included wheat, barley, turnips, clover, and peas.[2] For the WB region of Glamorgan, which included most of the Vale of Glamorgan and a narrow coastal strip of land to the west of the Ogwr river, Davies reported twenty-two different rotations.[3] Despite his statement later in the work that, as a result of the enthusiasm of enlightened proprietors and of inn-keepers on the London–Milford road who often managed extensive farms, turnips were well known and also well adapted to the soils of the area,[4] the crop occurs in only six of the rotations, not one of which was the Norfolk four-course. The major crops of the Vale were wheat and barley. In contrast with many other parts of Wales wheat was the bread corn; only in years of great dearth, such as 1800 and 1811, was barley used for bread making. The scarcity and high price of wheat stimulated its growth in the Vale and there are examples of land upon which the grain was grown for four years in succession in the early years of the century. The wheat acreage expanded at the expense of pastureland, and probably also of oats. Oats appeared in only nine of the rotations and the acreage devoted to the crop must have been considerably less than one-quarter that of wheat. In normal years wheat was exported northwards to the coalfield, where the rapidly growing industrial population provided a large market; barley, which was not much used locally, was sent in quantity to Bristol and elsewhere.[5] Clover was widely used as a one-year crop between two of grain, and peas were used nearly as often, though the smaller farmers still grew four grain crops successively. Beans

[1] Ibid., 156–7.
[2] C. Hassall, op. cit., 39–40, 48.
[3] W. Davies (1814, I), op. cit., 322–6, 338–40, 367, 371–2.
[4] Ibid., 514.
[5] Ibid., 339, 387, 481.

appeared in the rotations of the south-eastern part of the Vale and in those of the heavy soils near Pyle, where beans and wheat were alternated for as many as six years.

The beginnings of agricultural reform already recognized between 1794-96 and 1801 were consolidated by the dates of the octavo reports. In the Vale of Clwyd turnip husbandry was well established and green crops were liberally scattered through the rotations. Though oats were not of great importance in 1801, occupying less than 20 per cent, and in one small part less than 5 per cent, of the cropland, they had frequently ranked third (Figs. 15, 26). According to Davies's account they were little grown a few years later, presumably because of the adoption of the new methods. In south-east Monmouthshire, where turnip husbandry was already extensively employed at the turn of the century, Hassall's account is consistent with the 1801 survey, but in Glamorgan progress was not as swift. Although between 1796 and Davies's survey oats declined in importance and clover became widely used for one-year leys, turnips were not generally introduced. The many similarities between the 1810 report and the maps of the Acreage Return material suggest that what changes had occurred took place mainly between 1794 and 1801.

The Ingressive Regions not only contained the best tended arable land in Wales, but they were also areas in which animal husbandry was advanced. Both the permanent and the rotation grassland was of the highest quality and bore comparison favourably with that of other parts of Britain.[1] As in the other major regions the high prices and the wartime scarcity of arable crops led to the decline of the acreage under grass, but animal products still provided a considerable export trade. Fat cattle, sheep, and wool were distributed to surrounding areas and to the bigger markets but it was the dairy which was the focus of most farms with stock.[2]

When discussing agricultural improvements in Wales Davies summarized concisely the process which he had observed.[3] 'The greater proprietors formerly contented themselves with improving only the demesnes in their own occupation, and adorning the vicinity of their mansions in the reigning taste of the day, whether in planting,

[1] Ibid., 540-1, 592.
[2] W. Davies (1814, II), op. cit., 225, 250; C. Hassall, op. cit., 87, 90.
[3] Ibid., 117.

or in rooting up that which had been planted. Now the genius of agriculture inspires the resident nobility and gentry with a taste for general improvement, in which their tenantry are gradually instructed by example, which is far more efficacious than precept'. What Davies omitted was that the impact of agricultural reform was not felt uniformly throughout the country, either in time or in space; a consideration which has been one of the central themes of this and the previous chapter. By comparing the quarto and the octavo reports of the Board of Agriculture with the Acreage Returns of 1801 a rough idea of the chronology of crop-rotation improvement has emerged. It has been shown elsewhere that in parts of the English border counties, for example, in the district around Ross-on-Wye, Herefordshire, turnip husbandry became established before 1794[1] and the same is possibly true of south-east Monmouthshire. Certainly between the dates of the quarto reports and 1801 the new methods were adopted extensively in both south-east Monmouthshire and the Vale of Clwyd; in the Vale of Glamorgan turnip rotations were not widely accepted but oats declined in importance and short clover leys were introduced, modifying cropping practices considerably. Outside the Ingressive Regions the remarkable coincidence of the quarto reports and the Acreage Returns demonstrates that no changes took place. The period between the survey of 1801 and those which led to the octavo reports was one of more general progress. A collation of the two sets of data shows that within the Ingressive Regions it was a time of consolidation but elsewhere new methods had penetrated from the east bringing great changes. In eastern Peripheral Regions turnip husbandry became established upon the lighter soils, particularly in Denbighshire, Flintshire, and Monmouthshire; on the heavier land the older rotations persisted, though sometimes diversified by grass and clover leys. In the counties of the middle borderland especially, a longer-established crop, peas, also served to ameliorate grain rotations. The effects of the spirit of improvement decreased with distance to the west. In Glamorgan grass and clover leys were used in rotations but they were less evident in Carmarthenshire and south Pembrokeshire. In Cardiganshire, north-west Merioneth, and north Pembrokeshire, the most inaccessible parts of the Peripheral Regions, there is no

---

[1] D. Thomas, 'Agricultural changes in the Welsh Borderland: a cultural diffusion at the turn of the eighteenth century', *Transactions of the Honourable Society of Cymmrodorion* (1961), 111.

evidence of short leys and the only change seems to have been an increase in the acreage under wheat. Cropping in the Highland Regions was also modified in the decade after 1801, but only in the eastern parts. In Radnorshire turnips penetrated into the highest areas where arable working was practised and in other border shires wheat was introduced into the rotations, but these were scattered reforms. To the west of the moorland core cropping methods in the Highland Regions remained unchanged; a result of the combined effects of a severe physical setting and inaccessibility to the sources of agricultural improvement.

CHAPTER 11

THE TOPOGRAPHIES

THE value of the topographies is conditional. For the period before the writing of the Board of Agriculture reports, when little other data were available, they form major sources of information about agriculture,[1] but when compared with either the quarto or the octavo reports they are imprecise, not standardized and often ill-informed. Frequently the coverage lacks continuity and as reports upon agriculture usually appear only incidentally a great deal of the material is irrelevant. The usefulness of the work of the topographers in this study is therefore limited. At best they provide a means of checking the information derived from the Board of Agriculture reports and of giving perspective to that information by describing agricultural conditions before 1794.[2]

Few of the tours undertaken in Wales before the beginning of the Napoleonic wars led to accounts which give details of agriculture. A notable exception is provided by the two travel diaries of Arthur Young. The first, published in 1768, refers to a journey made in the previous summer along the south Wales littoral between Chepstow and Bridgend.[3] As one might expect from a man who later proved himself to be such a reliable and perceptive reporter of agricultural conditions the account is both detailed and knowledgeable. Though near Lydney, in Gloucestershire, Young described a rotation in which turnips were included, he does not mention the area to the west of Chepstow, where turnips had assumed an important place in the farming system by 1801.[4] Indeed he implies that, in comparison with the meadows, the arable land was of poor quality in this district.[5] To the west between Chepstow and Newport, in the area around Llanfaches, the standard of farming in Young's judgement was very mixed. The two most widely used rotations were first

---

[1] See, for example, H. C. Darby, 'Some early ideas on the agricultural regions of England', *Agricultural History Review*, 2 (1954), 30–2; G. E. Fussell and V. G. B. Atwater, 'Agriculture of rural England in the seventeenth century', *Economic Geography*, 9 (1933), 379–94; G. E. Fussell, 'Agriculture and economic geography in the eighteenth century', *Geographical Journal*, 74 (1929), 170–8.

[2] For a more general discussion of the value of the topographies of Wales at this period, see W. J. Hughes, *Wales and the Welsh in English Literature* (London, 1924), 84–100.

[3] A. Young, *A six weeks tour through the southern counties of England and Wales* (London, 1768)

[4] Supra, 154.   [5] A. Young, op. cit., 113–15.

year—fallow, second—wheat, third—barley, fourth—oats, fifth—
rye-grass and clover, to remain in pasture for from three to
eight years, and first year—fallow, second—wheat, third—barley,
fourth—clover, fifth—clover, sixth—wheat. The soils of the district
were dry and light, but few turnips were sown. The second rotation
was also used around Newport where the proportion of farmland
under grass was small.[1] For the north-western part of the Vale of
Glamorgan his report was critical and the area around Bridgend,
especially near Merthyr Mawr, evoked adverse comment. Though
there was much light land no turnips were grown, apart from those
of an English farmer who, despite his success, had no imitators.
The popular rotations in the north-west of the Vale were: first year—
wheat, second—barley, third—oats, fourth—oats, fifth—fallow, and
first year—wheat, second—barley, third—oats, fourth—peas or
beans. A few farmers used a better rotation: first year—wheat,
second—barley, third—clover, fourth—wheat.[2] Young made five
recommendations to the gentlemen of Glamorgan in the hope that,
by example, they would influence and improve agricultural practice
generally. First, he suggested that they should reform the management of their farms so that, for example, not too many draught
cattle were maintained. Secondly, he recommended the folding of
sheep. Thirdly, he argued that both turnip and carrot husbandry
was suited to many of the soils of the county and therefore should
be adopted. Fourthly, sainfoin was suggested as a sown grass
which would thrive upon limestone soils. And fifthly, the continuous cropping of wheat, oats, and barley was deplored and
two suitable rotations outlined: first year—turnips, second—barley,
third—clover, fourth—wheat, fifth—carrots, sixth—oats with sainfoin, and the Norfolk four-course.[3] These recommendations make
it clear that in Glamorgan not only was turnip husbandry unknown
and the arable cropped exhaustively, but the grazing land was
overstocked and badly managed, and grass or clover leys little used.

Young's second account is also outstandingly informative.[4] The
report was not published in the *Annals of Agriculture* until 1787 but,
in fact, it refers to a journey made eleven years earlier in 1776,

---

[1] Ibid., 115–17, 121.
[2] Ibid., 123–5.
[3] Ibid., 127–8.
[4] A Young, *Tours in England and Wales* (*selected from the Annals of Agriculture*),
No. 14 in a series of reprints of scarce tracts in economic and political science
(London, 1932), 1–57.

though additions were made to it as a result of a further tour in 1778. Young was returning from Ireland and travelled through south Wales by the Tywi–Usk route. In south Pembrokeshire clover was known and sometimes used but he saw no evidence of the cultivation of turnips. Between Milford Haven, his landing point, and Haverfordwest Young reported the following as the most common rotation: first year—fallow, second—wheat, third—peas or barley, fourth—barley or oats, fifth—oats, then a few farmers sowed clover but most allowed a sward to develop naturally, the land remaining under grass for five or seven years. At Slebech, between Haverfordwest and Narberth, he described a similar rotation: first year—fallow, second—wheat, third—barley, fourth—oats, fifth—clover, then under pasture for two or three years; but beyond Narberth oats were omitted from the course. In this area the growing of potatoes was increasing and clover was also being used more.[1] In lowland Carmarthenshire cropping methods were much the same. Wheat, barley, oats, clover, and sometimes peas followed a fallow and leys of three years generally divided one crop course from the next.[2] In the whole of his journey through Pembrokeshire and Carmarthenshire Young saw less than 20 acres of turnips, but near Brecon, though the crop had not been commonly adopted, there were signs of the beginnings of improvement under the stimulus of the agricultural society. Both turnips and clover had been introduced and the secretary of the society had bought twenty ewes from Bakewell. In the Wye valley near Hay turnips were also being introduced and together with a rotation very similar to those in south-west Wales Young described one in which turnips were followed by two crops of barley and then three years of clover.[3] He was less pleased with agriculture in Monmouthshire, where between Raglan—'the turning off for Chepstow'—and Monmouth turnips were only occasionally cropped but grains were grown for several years on the same ground.[4]

When compared with the reports of the many other tours which were published so frequently at this time, the quality of Young's accounts becomes evident. Such surveys as those of Wyndham[5] and

[1] Ibid. 1–5.
[2] Ibid., 11, 13.
[3] Ibid., 17–20.
[4] Ibid., 21.
[5] H. P. Wyndham, *A tour through Momouthshire and Wales* (Salisbury, 1781).

Cradock,[1] which appeared shortly after Young's first report, though often quite lengthy and covering a great deal of ground, rarely give details of agriculture. The most explicit statement which Cradock, for example, made in his whole report was to mention that the vales of Montgomeryshire 'abound in corn and are luxuriant in pasturage'. But it is when Young's accounts are collated with the quarto reports of the Board of Agriculture and the 1801 returns that their real value as research material becomes clear, because for a limited area in south Wales the comparison throws light upon agricultural trends in the twenty years before the beginning of the Napoleonic wars. His descriptions of Monmouthshire, except for the south-east where turnips had not appeared in the rotations in 1767, seem to correspond closely with the picture in 1794 and 1801. For example, though the 1801 return for the parish of Llanfaches is lost, the return of the adjacent parish of St. Bride's Netherwent results in a crop combination index of WB, with oats as the third rank crop (Figs. 26, 28); precisely what one would expect from Young's account.

The same coincidence between Young's reports and the later surveys is also evident in the other counties of south Wales. In Brecknockshire turnip culture was shown to be established but not extensive in the valleys of the Wye and Usk in both 1794 and 1801 (Fig. 22), and in the parish of Hay barley occupied over 35 per cent of the cropland. In the Vale of Glamorgan Young's description tallies with that of Fox in 1796, both in the details of crops grown and in the criticism of the management of grazing land, though, of course, by 1801 many changes had taken place. To the west in Carmarthenshire and south Pembrokeshire there was a continuity of practice through to the date of the Acreage Returns. As in 1776–78, the acreage of turnips was small in both counties in 1801; potatoes, on the other hand, were almost everywhere fourth crop, often exceeded 5 per cent of the cropland, and in Haverfordwest occupied 23 per cent of the cropland (Figs. 22, 27). Young's rotations are also reflected in the crop combination map (Fig. 28) where, in south Pembrokeshire, most parishes are designated WOB, though in Carmarthenshire he seems not to have noticed that wheat was less important (Fig. 12), probably because his traverse of the

[1] J. Cradock, *An account of some of the most romantic parts of north Wales* (London, 1777).

county was confined to the valleys of the Taf and Tywi and his attention focused upon the land of the better farmers. However, the substantial agreement between the surveys of 1767–78 and those of 1794–96 and 1801 is sufficient to establish that there was little improvement of agricultural methods in the years before the Napoleonic wars, and that the changes, already described, which took place during the war in many parts of Wales were, by comparison, momentous.

Fortunately, for the period of the Napoleonic wars, when travel in continental Europe was restricted, many more topographies of Wales appeared, though proportionately the number of reports useful in this study did not increase greatly. Of the large number of accounts published[1] barely half a dozen give any tangible evidence about agriculture. Most, like the work of Pratt who toured Wales in the early years of the war,[2] are dominated by antiquarian and romantic reflection in which the lives and occupations of the unsophisticated 'foreigners' were often as idealized as the mock-heroic descriptions of the countryside. Warner was one of those who was more realistic. Like Walter Davies he was a priest of the Established Church and a prolific writer. He undertook two walking tours of Wales, one in August 1797 and the second in the following summer. In his account of the first tour, apart from a brief description of the improvements of one owner in the Vale of Ffestiniog,[3] there is little of value on the agricultural scene, but the account of his second tour, which took him through most parts of Wales, is most useful. One of his few references to agriculture in the upland areas was a description of the life of a peasant who lived near Bwlch y Groes, between Llanymawddwy and Llanuwchllyn, Merioneth,[4] that is, in part of what has previously been described as the western Highland Regions. The area was among the most inaccessible in Wales, and until the making of the turnpike road along which Warner travelled the use of wheeled carts was hardly known, the pony-drawn sled

---

[1] For full lists of topographies of Wales, see J. P. Anderson, *The book of British topography* (London, 1881), 334–53; A. H. Dodd, *The industrial revolution in north Wales* (Cardiff, 1933), xxv–xxvii; G. E. Fussell, *The exploration of England. A select bibliography of travel and topography: 1570–1815* (London, 1935); Hughes, op. cit., 189–200; Appendices to the report of the Royal Commission on land in Wales and Monmouthshire, *Parliamentary Papers*, 33 (1896), 647–53.

[2] S. J. Pratt, *Gleanings through Wales, Holland and Westphalia*, 4 vols. (London, 1795).

[3] R. Warner, *A walk through Wales in August 1797* (Bath, 1799), 117–18.

[4] R. Warner, *A second walk through Wales* (Bath, 1799), 185–8.

being the chief means of haulage. In 1798 peat was still transported by sled from the mountain tops to the homesteads near the valley bottoms, where it was the universal fuel. Agricultural methods were equally primitive. The small patches of arable were tilled not with the plough but by spade, and the hand-barrow was the main mechanical aid. Each worker usually owned a cow and a pig, but meat was rarely part of his diet. Oaten cakes, bread made of a mixture of rye and wheat flour, cheese, and potatoes were the principal constituents of his food and butter-milk and beer his drinks. Occasionally, even in the western uplands, 'spirited proprietors' well in advance of local methods introduced exotic systems of agriculture. Warner describes the estate of probably the best known of these in west Wales, Thomas Johnes of Hafod, Cardiganshire.[1] Of his very large estate Johnes farmed nearly 5,000 acres himself and as well as extensive landscaping he undertook ambitious draining and reclamation schemes. Rough ground was enclosed, drained, limed, ploughed, and then sown with turnips. Sheep were folded upon the crop and after manuring the land, potatoes then oats or barley followed before grass seeds were sown to establish a pasture. The practices of Johnes seem to be reflected in the 1801 returns where, for the very rugged parish of Ysbyty Ystwyth, turnips occupied over 2 per cent of the cropland; a figure reached by few other parishes in Cardiganshire, even in the lowland parts of the county (Fig. 22). He was also interested in the improvement of livestock and introduced a cross between the Cheviot and Ryeland breeds of sheep into north Cardiganshire, but his particular concern was afforestation, which he pursued by methods most advanced for the time. He normally planted 300,000 trees every year but in 1797 he had planted nearly twice that number, mainly larch. It is not surprising that Warner considered the husbandry of surrounding farms, by comparison, to be 'miserably carried on'.

Warner's references to agriculture in the Peripheral Regions are more widespread but less precise. The general tone of his account confirms the evidence of the quarto Board of Agriculture reports and the 1801 returns that little progress had been made in agricultural improvement. In Anglesey agriculture was 'a languid, spiritless, unprofitable system; the consequences of which are too visible in scanty crops and a poverty-striken peasantry'. Only upon

[1] Ibid., 150–4, Johnes was a correspondent of Arthur Young; supra, 42, Fig. 7.

the estates of a few owners (Panton, Arthur Young's correspondent in Anglesey was cited as an example),[1] were the new methods in use.[2] South Cardiganshire he found equally impoverished, especially the fishing villages fringing Cardigan Bay,[3] but rather surprisingly his report of Pembrokeshire north of the Presely range was most favourable; the standard of husbandry was high, crops were good, and the farm workers were contented, mainly, it seems, due to the benevolence of the landowners.[4] For Carmarthenshire he confirms that oats and butter in great quantities were exported to Bristol, London, and other places.[5]

Warner travelled through both the Ingressive Regions of Denbighshire and Glamorgan. With the Vale of Clwyd he was most impressed. His visit came towards the end of his tour and he was of the opinion that nowhere else in Wales was husbandry so advanced; it stimulated ideas of 'population, plenty and unbounded fertility'.[6] This pronouncement adds greater weight to the view already expressed, that in his report to the Board of Agriculture on Denbighshire Kay completely underrated the progress in agriculture which had been made in the Vale of Clwyd, owing to a lack of first hand knowledge of conditions there. Warner was less enthusiastic about the Vale of Glamorgan. Like Young, he criticises severely the exhausting rotations used, in which as many as four crops of grain were taken successively, but he did suggest that better methods, more consistent with the natural fertility of the area, were being introduced, and quoted one example at Boverton.[7]

In the same year, 1798, Evans undertook the first of his two tours of Wales, through the northern part of the country. Beginning at Shrewsbury he travelled westwards along the Vale of Severn, and after touring Snowdonia returned by the Vale of Llangollen. He made little reference to agriculture during the account of his journey but towards the end of the volume of letters which were the result of his observations, he included one dealing specifically with agriculture.[8] His approach was not that of Warner, who gave detailed

[1] Supra, 39, Fig. 7.
[2] R. Warner (second walk), op. cit., 300–1.
[3] Ibid., 328–9.
[4] Ibid., 340–1.
[5] Ibid., 356.
[6] Ibid., 196.
[7] Ibid., 57–61.
[8] J. Evans, *A tour through part of north Wales in the year 1798* (London, 1800), 367–82.

descriptions of scattered places, but attempted to give a more synoptic evaluation. His general impression of agriculture in north Wales is summed up in his assertion that 'agriculture is at a very low ebb; it appears to have experienced little improvement for centuries, and the Welsh farmer has the very first principles of good husbandry to learn'. He complained of the methods of arable management, of the neglect of sheep folding, of the need for enclosures, and of the scarcity and improper application of manures. As a remedy he recommended that landlords should stimulate reform by granting long leases to their tenants, lending small sums of money to defray the costs of improvement and by giving bounties to those who had shown enterprise. Evans's report is consistent with what has been gleaned from other sources, but it should be noted that he did not travel through the Vale of Clwyd. In his tour of south Wales, five years later in 1803, Evans travelled through the Vale of Glamorgan to west Pembrokeshire, then northwards to Aberystwyth and returned by way of Brecknockshire and the Vale of Usk. Again he considered the general state of agriculture in a special section and enumerated at some length the faults which he detected.[1] In addition to the complaints he made about north Wales, he deplored the absence of marling, a practice which English farmers employed so successfully, the lack of proper drainage schemes, the primitive implements of husbandry and, above all, the insufficient attention given to silviculture and afforestation. Evans's view that Glamorgan was the most advanced county of south Wales was not, however, shared by Malkin, who travelled roughly the same route in the same year. Malkin held that the gentlemen farmers of Brecknockshire, Cardiganshire, Carmarthenshire, and Pembrokeshire were more progressive and that, despite the natural advantages of the Vale of Glamorgan, improvement there was slow.[2] The possibility of error in accepting generalized opinions about agricultural conditions at this time is evident.

Several other accounts of tours add small details to the picture of agriculture during the Napoleonic wars. For example, Lipscomb provides a reminder of the large-scale rural depopulation under way

---

[1] J. Evans, *Letters written during a tour through south Wales in the year 1803* (London, 1804), 415–34.
[2] B. H. Malkin, *The scenery, antiquities and biography of south Wales, from materials collected during two excursions in the year 1803* (London, 1804), 59–60; cf. 201–2, 264–5, 319–21.

13

at this period in his description of a family forced to leave the countryside to seek work elsewhere.[1] But the only remaining major source is not a travel diary, but an attempt to provide a general description of the history and conditions of the counties of England and Wales. *The beauties of England and Wales* was published in eighteen volumes between 1801 and 1815. It was edited, and to a large extent written, by E. W. Brayley and J. Britton and dealt with each county in turn. The account of the towns, parks, and other notable features of the county was prefaced by a brief history and a systematic treatment of the physical and human setting. In this section a short description of agriculture usually appeared; sometimes copied from the Board of Agriculture reports, sometimes copied from another work, and sometimes what appears to be an original commentary on the state of husbandry in the county. One whole volume deals with the six counties of north Wales,[2] one with six counties of south Wales,[3] while Monmouthshire is studied in a third volume.[4] It is a remarkable coincidence that the areas covered in each volume, and their dates of publication correspond closely with those of the octavo Board of Agriculture reports by Davies and Hassall. It was originally intended that John Evans,[5] who wrote the account of north Wales and also that of Monmouthshire in the volume for which he and Britton were jointly responsible, should write the description of south Wales, but he died before the work was finished and Thomas Rees was appointed as his successor. Evans was an experienced traveller and topographer, and his account of agriculture in north Wales seems to be mainly the result of his own observations,[6] but the study of south Wales by Rees, who had not previously published a topography of any part of Great Britain, relies heavily upon both acknowledged and unacknowledged borrowing from other sources.

The descriptions of the land included within the Highland Regions are not very helpful. Rees reported on upland Radnorshire[7] but his account is a paraphrase, too close to leave any doubts about its

---

[1] G. Lipscomb, *A journey into south Wales* (London, 1802), 101–3.

[2] J. Evans, *The beauties of England and Wales – north Wales* (London, 1812), XVII.

[3] T. Rees, *The beauties of England and Wales – south Wales* (London, 1815), XVIII.

[4] J. Britton and J. Evans, *The beauties of England and Wales* (London, 1810), XI.

[5] I.e. John Evans, B.A., of Jesus College, Oxford, who toured Wales in 1798 and 1803.

[6] But see also *The dictionary of Welsh biography down to 1940* (London, 1959), *sub nom.* Evans, John (1768–c. 1812), 242.

[7] T. Rees, op. cit., 878–9.

origins, of Clark's quarto report of 1794. Only Evans, in his accounts of Merioneth and Caernarvonshire, appears to give an independent picture of conditions in the uplands. In Merioneth several of the extensive areas of mountain grazing had become private property and enclosed with dry-stone walls. Other sheep walks were still open and served both to carry large flocks and to provide peat for fuel.[1] The enclosure movement in the neighbouring county of Caernarvonshire does not seem to have progressed sufficiently, by the date of Evans's survey, to break down the traditional system of transhumance. *Hafotai*, summer huts or cottages from which the men tended their flocks and sometimes tilled the land and the women cared for the dairy cattle and goats, were still used only seasonally,[2] whereas in most places in the east of the country they had already become permanent dwellings.

In the western Peripheral Regions many instances of improvement are reported but with some reservations about the general standard of husbandry. While in Anglesey the output from both arable and pasture had increased, Evans complained that the potential production had not been realized because reclamation schemes had not been undertaken on a large enough scale. In many areas considerable tracts remained to be drained and in others stretches of coastal, blown sands were unused, when they might, with proper treatment, have been employed as meadow or for the growing of hemp and flax.[3] In lowland Caernarvonshire, and especially Llŷn, Evans was pleased with the progress. There was still a prejudice against clover leys, and green crops, including turnips, were slow in finding a place in the popular rotations, but two crops, wheat and potatoes, had recently been introduced and were increasing in popularity. The acreage under potatoes, particularly, had increased and there was no longer a need to import the crop into the Vale of Conway and the hinterland of Caernarvon to supply local deficiencies; exports from the county were now sent to Liverpool.[4] In Merioneth and Cardiganshire the reports support the view, derived from the Board of Agriculture and 1801 surveys, that in these inaccessible counties advances were confined to the domains of enlightened landowners.

[1] J. Evans (1812), op. cit., 891–2.
[2] Ibid., 319.
[3] Ibid., 155–6.
[4] Ibid., 318–34.

13*

In Merioneth considerable effort had been expended in the draining and enclosure of coastal marsh[1] while in Cardiganshire, such
owners as Johnes had transformed the land directly under their
control;[2] but elsewhere improvements were adopted tardily.

The more extensive improvements in the eastern and southern
Peripheral Regions are also reflected in this topography, where they
are attributed to the vigour of reforming landlords, often working
through one of a number of well-established agricultural societies.
It is true that at least two societies existed at this date in the west,
in Caernarvonshire and Cardiganshire,[3] but both were new and had
most of their work yet to do. In Denbighshire, on the other hand,
a number of societies flourished under the patronage of Sir Watkin
Williams Wynn and, together with the Vale of Clwyd, they had
influenced profoundly the area around Wrexham.[4] Brecknockshire
provides another good example of a county where many of the
improvements were a direct result of the efforts of the agricultural
society which, by offering premiums, had encouraged the growth
of turnips, clover, and potatoes, and also the breeding of better
livestock.[5] In more westerly counties like Carmarthenshire, which is
not credited with an agricultural society, new methods were being
introduced rather slowly in the lowlands; areas such as the Vales
of Gwendraeth Fach, Llwchwr, and Tywi, and the district around
St. Clears.[6] It is unfortunate that for the remaining parts of the
eastern and south Peripheral Regions the accounts are based upon
earlier works, usually the quarto reports of the Board of Agriculture.

Finally, in Evans's description of the Ingressive Region of Denbighshire, the Vale of Clwyd, he makes it clear that he was very
favourably impressed both by the standard of the husbandry of the
area and by its fertility. Here again the scanty treatment of the
county in Kay's quarto report is revealed by a contemporary
writer, and he is said to have 'overlooked, or much under-rated the
improvements in this part of the island'.[7]

The accounts of the topographers, though their status as research
documents is similar in some ways to that of the ballad with which

¹ Ibid., 892–3.
² T. Rees, op. cit., 400–8.
³ J. Evans (1812), op. cit., 334; T. Rees, op. cit., 408.
⁴ J. Evans (1812), op. cit., 517.
⁵ T. Rees, op. cit., 58.
⁶ Ibid., 273–4.
⁷ J. Evans (1812), op. cit., 517–8.

this work began, do lend weight, if only in a fragmentary and qualitative way, to the conclusions derived from the other surveys. They confirm that in Wales before the beginning of the Napoleonic wars there were few improvers and little improvement. Between 1793 and 1815 they recorded successively the wave of new ideas and new techniques which broke upon the east of the country and decreased in momentum with distance and height. But while they recognized the changes none of the topographers seems to have been aware of the economic, political, and social forces which gave power and purpose to the flow; none perceived what Lowe pointed out so succinctly in 1822: 'Of all the departments of our national industry, none received so continued a stimulus from the war as agriculture. Our manufactures, particularly those of cotton and hardware, experienced at all times a greater impulse; but the nature of manufacture admitting of more speedily increasing supply in proportion to demand, the briskness was often temporary, and followed by a season of discouragement. Our tillage, on the other hand, was hardly at any time brought on a par with our increasing population, so that the stimulant of a demand, equal to or greater than the internal supply, prevailed throughout almost the whole period'.[1]

[1] J. Lowe, *The present state of England in regard to agriculture, trade and finance* (London, 1822), 133–4.

EPILOGUE

IN this study an attempt has been made to re-create the agricultural geography of Wales during the Napoleonic wars. The material upon which the work rests varies considerably in its detail, uniformity, coverage, and objectiveness, and special attention has been paid to methods of analysis. Greatest emphasis has been placed upon the evidence provided by the Acreage Returns of 1801, giving crop acreage information by parishes, but the conclusions derived from this source have been tested by comparisons with the other major surveys, enquiries which have also served to supplement the limited scope of the 1801 statistics. The statistical and cartographical techniques adopted in the analysis of the 1801 acreages have, on the one hand, provided a means of overcoming the inherent deficiencies of the returns, and on the other, enabled their presentation in a summary form in which it was possible to identify crop combination regions. The crop regions then provided a rational framework within which to discuss most of the remaining material. It is true that the evidence available for the period of the Napoleonic wars is fragmentary and heavily biased in favour of the tilled land, though cropping in many parts of Wales was limited, but there does emerge a regional picture of Welsh agriculture, sufficiently clear for both changes and continuity of geographic values to be recognized.

It was the great inflation during the Napoleonic wars which provided the direct stimulus to many of the rapid agricultural changes of the period. Most of the changes had been underway long before the turn of the century but they were speeded by the high wartime prices. For example, between 1793 and 1815, the enclosure movement in Wales reached its peak and between the same years the drift of agricultural workers to the industrial towns was accelerated. But the changes and reforms by no means obliterated all that had existed before. Though the new husbandry was spreading most vigorously from lowland England into Wales, there still prevailed, especially in the west where many areas were physically inaccessible to the eastern lowlands, an older order in which elements of earlier diffusions persisted. There resulted the major differences in agricultural practice between east and west which many of the distribution maps have revealed.

One of the most striking features to emerge from this study is the influence which physical conditions exerted upon the utilization of land; a factor which operated as strongly in areas of agricultural change as in areas of agricultural stability. This was evident in the study of crop distribution and was also shown in the more detailed examples of farm and field patterns in the major crop regions. In the spread of new crops and new agricultural methods into Wales there were clearly both ecological and technological controls, while the barrier created by the mountain spine of the country was of great geographical importance.

From the statistical, cartographic, and literary material available it has been possible to show the impress of the powerful forces of change, operating during the Napoleonic wars, upon the Welsh countryside. The forces varied in strength from place to place; the land which they affected was physically multifarious and agriculturally diverse. The result was the complex and contrasting agriculture which this study has attempted to outline.

BIBLIOGRAPHY

THE following list is not exhaustive. It is selected from the most recent and readily available published studies dealing with the sources used in this work, arranged under the materials to which they refer.

Minor sources

G. D. AMERY, 'The writings of Arthur Young', *Journal of the Royal Agricultural Society of England*, 85 (1924), 175–205.

G. E. FUSSELL, 'My impressions of Arthur Young', *Agricultural History*, 17 (1943), 135–44.

W. E. MINCHINTON, 'Agricultural returns and the government during the Napoleonic wars', *Agricultural History Review*, 1 (1953), 29–43.

D. THOMAS, 'Arthur Young on Wales', *Bulletin of the Board of Celtic Studies* (in the press).

The Acreage Returns of 1801

P. A. CHURLEY, 'The Yorkshire Crop Returns of 1801', *Yorkshire Bulletin of Economic and Social Research*, 5 (1953–54), 179–96.

K. G. DAVIES and G. E. FUSSELL, 'Worcestershire in the Acreage Returns for 1801', *Transactions of the Worcestershire Archaeological Society*, 27 (1951), 15–23.

J. P. DODD, 'The state of agriculture in Shropshire, 1775–1825', *Transactions of the Shropshire Archaeological Society*, 55 (1954), 1–31.

D. B. GRIGG, 'The 1801 Crop Returns for south Lincolnshire', *East Midland Geographer*, 16 (1961), 43–8.

H. C. K. HENDERSON, 'The 1801 Crop Returns for Wiltshire', *Wiltshire Archaeological and Natural History Magazine*, 54 (1951), 85–91.

——, 'The 1801 Crop Returns: geographical distributions', *Transactions of the Leicestershire Archaeological Society*, 27 (1951), 100–2.

——, 'The 1801 Crop Returns for Sussex', *Sussex Archaeological Collections*, 90 (1952), 51–9.

——, 'Agriculture in England and Wales in 1801', *Geographical Journal*, 118 (1952), 338–45.

——, 'The agricultural geography of Derbyshire in the early nineteenth century', *East Midland Geographer*, 7 (1957), 16–20.

W. G. HOSKINS, 'The Leicestershire Crop Returns of 1801' (included in *Studies in Leicestershire agrarian history*), *Transactions of the Leicestershire Archaeological Society*, 24 (1948), 127–53.

W. E. MINCHINTON, 'Agriculture in Gloucestershire during the Napoleonic wars', *Transactions of the Bristol and Gloucestershire Archaeological Society*, 68 (1949), 165–83.

——, 'Agriculture in Dorset during the Napoleonic wars', *Proceedings of the Dorset Natural History and Archaeological Society*, 77 (1955), 162–73.

R. A. Pelham, 'The 1801 Crop Returns for Staffordshire in their geographical setting', *Collections for a History of Staffordshire* (1950–51), 231–42.

——, 'The agricultural geography of Warwickshire during the Napoleonic wars', *Transactions of the Birmingham Archaeological Society*, 68 (1952), 89–106.

——, 'The agricultural revolution in Hampshire with special reference to the Acreage Returns of 1801', *Papers and Proceedings of the Hampshire Field Club and Archaeological Society*, 18 (1953), 139–53.

D. Thomas, 'The Acreage Returns of 1801 for Wales: an addendum', *Bulletin of the Board of Celtic Studies*, 17 (1956–58), 50–2.

——, 'The statistical and cartographic treatment of the Acreage Returns of 1801', *Geographical Studies*, 5 (1958), 15–25.

——, 'The Acreage Returns of 1801 for the Welsh borderland', *Transactions and Papers, 1959*, Institute of British Geographers, 26 (1959), 169–83.

——, 'The Acreage Returns of 1801: a test of accuracy', *Bulletin of the Board of Celtic Studies*, 18 (1958–60), 379–83.

D. Williams, 'The Acreage Returns of 1801 for Wales', *Bulletin of the Board of Celtic Studies*, 14 (1950–52), 54–68, 139–54.

The early Censuses

H. C. Darby, 'The movement of population to and from Cambridgeshire between 1851 and 1861', *Geographical Journal*, 101 (1943), 118–25.

E. W. Gilbert, 'The growth of inland and seaside health resorts in England', *Scottish Geographical Magazine*, 55 (1939), 16–35.

M. C. Gilpin, 'Population changes around the shores of Milford Haven from 1800 to the present day', *Field Studies*, 1 (1960), 23–36.

H. J. Habakkuk, 'English population in the eighteenth century', *Economic History Review*, 2nd series, 6 (1953–54), 117–33.

J. W. House, *North-eastern England: population movements and the landscape since the early nineteenth century* (Newcastle upon Tyne, 1954).

J. H. Johnson, 'The population of Londonderry during the great Irish famine', *Economic History Review*, 2nd series, 10 (1957–58), 273–85.

——, 'Marriage and fertility in nineteenth century Londonderry', *Journal of the Statistical and Social Inquiry Society of Ireland*, 20 (1957–58), 99–117.

R. Lawton, 'Population movements in the west Midlands, 1841–1861', *Geography*, 43 (1958), 164–77.

T. H. Marshall, 'The population problem during the industrial revolution', *Economic History*, 1 (1926–29), 429–56.

N. J. G. Pounds, 'Population movement in Cornwall, and the use of mining in the eighteenth century', *Geography*, 28 (1943), 37–46.

J. A. Sheppard, 'East Yorkshire's agricultural labour force in the mid-nineteenth century', *Agricultural History Review*, 9 (1961), 43–54.

A. E. Smailes, 'Population changes in the colliery districts of Northumberland and Durham since 1800', *Geographical Journal*, 91 (1938), 220–32.

C. T. Smith, 'The movement of population in England and Wales in 1851 and 1861', *Geographical Journal*, 117 (1951), 200–10.

B. Thomas, 'Migration of labour into the Glamorgan coalfield, 1861–1891', *Economica*, 10 (1930), 275–94.

A. E. TRUEMAN, 'Population changes in the eastern part of the south Wales coalfield', *Geographical Journal*, 53 (1919), 410–19.

H. R. WILKINSON, 'The mapping of Census returns of occupations and industries', *Geography*, 37 (1952), 37–46.

Guides to official sources, No. 2, Census reports of Great Britain 1801–1931 (H.M.S.O., London, 1951).

Manuscript maps and plans

SIR C. CLOSE, *The early years of the Ordnance Survey* (Chatham, 1926).

M. DAVIES, 'Field patterns in the Vale of Glamorgan', *Transactions of the Cardiff Naturalists' Society*, 84 (1954–55), 5–14.

W. R. MEAD, 'Ridge and furrow in Buckinghamshire', *Geographical Journal*, 120 (1954), 34–42.

H. C. PRINCE, 'The changing landscape of Panshanger', *East Herts. Archaeological Society*, 14 (1959), 42–58.

L. D. STAMP (ed.), *The land of Britain*, Report of the Land Utilisation Survey of Britain, 93 parts (London, 1936–50). E.g. J. May and S. F. Wells, *Montgomeryshire*, 36 (London, 1942), 350.

E. M. YATES, 'History in a map', *Geographical Journal*, 126 (1960), 32–51.

Enclosure awards

M. W. BERESFORD, 'Commissioners of enclosure', *Economic History Review*, 15 (1946), 130–40.

I. BOWEN, *The great enclosures of common lands in Wales* (London, 1914).

W. H. R. CURTLER, *The enclosure and redistribution of our land* (Oxford, 1920).

A. H. DODD, 'The enclosure movement in north Wales', *Bulletin of the Board of Celtic Studies*, 3 (1925–27), 216–38.

——, *The industrial revolution in north Wales* (Cardiff, 1933), 53–88.

S. R. EYRE, 'The upward limit of enclosure on the East Moor of north Derbyshire', *Transactions and Papers, 1957*, Institute of British Geographers, 23 (1957), 61–74.

E. C. K. GONNER, *Common land and enclosure* (London, 1912).

E. J. JONES, 'The enclosure movement in Angelsey (1788–1866)', *Transactions of the Angelsey Antiquarian Society and Field Club* (1925), 21–58; (1926), 51–89.

T. I. J. JONES, *Acts of parliament concerning Wales* (Cardiff, 1959), 276–99.

D. R. MILLS, 'Enclosures in Kesteven', *Agricultural History Review*, 7 (1959), 82–97.

C. S. ORWIN and C. S. ORWIN, *The open fields* (Oxford, 1954).

G. SLATER, *The English peasantry and the enclosure of common fields* (London, 1907).

——, 'The inclosure of common fields considered geographically', *Geographical Journal*, 29 (1907), 35–55.

W. E. TATE, 'The cost of parliamentary enclosure in England', *Economic History Review*, 2nd series, 5 (1952–53), 258–65.

J. G. THOMAS, 'The distribution of the commons in part of Arwystli at the time of enclosure', *Montgomeryshire Collections*, 54 (1955), 27–33.

——, 'Some enclosure patterns in central Wales', *Geography*, 42 (1957), 25–36.

The Board of Agriculture reports

J. H. CLAPHAM, *An economic history of modern Britain* (Cambridge, 1950), I, 12–34.

H. C. DARBY, 'Some early ideas on the agricultural regions of England', *Agricultural History Review*, 2 (1954), 43–7.

W. G. EAST, 'Land utilization in England at the end of the eighteenth century', *Geographical Journal*, 89 (1937), 156–72.

A. M. LAMBERT, 'The agriculture of Oxfordshire at the end of the eighteenth century', *Agricultural History*, 29 (1955), 31–8.

W. SMITH, *An economic geography of Great Britain* (London, 1959), 16–42.

D. THOMAS, 'Agricultural changes in the Welsh Borderland: a cultural diffusion at the turn of the eighteenth century', *Transactions of the Honourable Society of Cymmrodorion* (1961), 101–14.

D. WILLIAMS, *The Rebecca riots* (Cardiff, 1955), 62–83.

The Topographies

J. P. ANDERSON, *The book of British topography* (London, 1881).

G. E. FUSSELL, 'Agriculture and economic geography in the eighteenth century', *Geographical Journal*, 74 (1929), 170–8.

——, *The exploration of England. A select bibliography of travel and topography: 1570–1815* (London, 1935).

——, 'The English countryside and population in the eighteenth century', *Economic Geography*, 12 (1936), 294–300, 411–30.

——, 'Animal husbandry in the eighteenth century', *Agricultural History*, 11 (1937), 96–116, 189–214.

G. E. FUSSELL and V. G. B. ATWATER, 'Agriculture of rural England in the seventeenth century', *Economic Geography*, 9 (1933), 379–94.

G. E. FUSSELL and C. GOODMAN, 'Traffic in farm products in eighteenth-century England, except livestock and livestock products', *Agricultural History*, 12 (1938), 355–68.

——, Crop husbandry in eighteenth-century England', *Agricultural History*, 15 (1941), 202–16; 16 (1942), 41–63.

W. J. HUGHES, *Wales and the Welsh in English literature* (London, 1924), 84–100.

INDEX

rivers, 30.
road traffic, 13–14.
roads, 30, 77.
Romans, 14.
Ross-on-Wye, 168.
rotations, improved, 7, 157, 158, 160–2, 163–4, 171; see also Norfolk four-course.
rough pasture, 30, 115, 116, 117, 118, 120, 121, 122, 123, 125, 130, 136–7.
routeways, mid Wales, 70, 126–8.
  north Wales coast, 14, 84, 89, 126–8.
  south Wales coast, 13–14, 84, 126–8, 166.
  Usk-Tywi, 14, 172.
Roy, General W., 29.
Rutland, 130.
rye, 20, 25, 39, 58, 69–70, 72, 81, 85–6, 91, 93, 117, 149, 122, 146–7, 155, 158.
  import of, 48.
  price of, 3.
  yield of, 41, 42.
rye-grass, 147, 149, 151, 153, 160, 171.

sainfoin, 155, 171.
St. Andrews Major, 129.
St. Asaph, 166.
  diocese of, 20.
  parish of, 54, 125, 126.
St. Bride's Netherwent, 173.
St. David's, diocese of, 20, 69.
Severn, river, 13, 83, 127, 139, 140.
  Vale of, 77, 89, 106, 110.
sheep, 15, 42, 43, 121, 148, 152, 155, 160, 167, 171, 175, 177, 179.
  Cheviot, 175.
  Ryeland, 175.
shipping industry, 109–10.
Silurian, 63, 117, 124.
Sinclair, Sir J., 7, 17–18, 34.
Skenfrith, hundred of, 22, 109.
Slater, G., 130.
Slebech, 172.
sled, pony-drawn, 174–5.
slopes, steep, 117, 119, 122, 123.
smelting, 11.
Smith, A., 7.
snow, 39.

Snowdonia, 36, 100.
soils, 77, 120, 125.
  acid, 65, 68, 69, 70, 124.
  alkaline, 69, 70, 72, 74, 84, 124.
  alluvial, 74.
  Coal Measure, 162.
  heavy, 64, 65, 72, 74, 77, 92, 124, 150, 162, 164, 167, 168.
  light, 60, 63, 72, 75, 77, 124, 162, 164, 168, 171.
  map of, 124.
  thin, 117.
soup kitchens, 43.
Speenhamland system, 8–10.
squatting, 123, 132, 134, 136, 139.
starch, 5.
Statistical account of Scotland, 18.
statistical evidence, 17–29, 39–112.
stocks, 19.
  of grain, 40, 43, 48, 49, 50, 51.
straw, 42.
  price of, 39.
Suffolk, 17.
Swansea, 84, 102, 103.
  hundred of, 103, 109.

Taf, Vale of, 174.
Talgarth, hundred of, 104, 108–9, 150.
taxation, 5.
Telford, T., 14.
Teifi, Vale of, 71, 160.
temperature, 63, 70, 74.
  accumulated, 59, 65.
tenants, 77.
Tenby, 29.
The Beauties of England and Wales, 35, 178–80.
Thomas, J. G., 131–3.
Tithe Redemption Commission, 30, 128–9.
tithes, 34, 42, 54.
topographies, 33, 35–6, 170–81.
Traeth Mawr, 138.
transhumance, 118, 141, 148, 179.
Trecastell, 159.
Tredegar, 103.
Trefilan, parish of, 56, 119–21.
trefoil, 155.
Tre-lech a'r Betws, parish of, 57.